Far-Back Mornings

KEYS TO READING

fires of far-back mornings

CARL SANDBURG

Louise Matteoni

Wilson H. Lane

Floyd Sucher

Versie G. Burns

Theodore L. Harris, *Advisory Author*

Harold B. Allen, *Linguistic Consultant*

THE ECONOMY COMPANY   Oklahoma City   Indianapolis   Orange, CA

Design: James Stockton

Cover Illustration: Jon Goodell

Permission to use or adapt copyrighted material appearing in
this book is gratefully acknowledged on pages 318-320, which
are hereby made a part of this copyright page.

ISBN 0-8332-1288-5

THE ECONOMY COMPANY, Educational Publishers
1901 North Walnut   Oklahoma City, Oklahoma 73125

Contents

THE BUTCHER, THE BAKER, THE COMPUTER PROGRAMMER

THROUGH A KALEIDOSCOPE

HOW YOU PLAY THE GAME

MIRROR, MIRROR

CONSIDER THE CHAMELEON

LOOK BEHIND YOU

The Butcher, the Baker, the Computer Programmer

Hai Lu and the Necklace

Hai Lu ran up the stairs. From behind, someone called him; he recognized Wing Loy, his friend. Wing Loy's father had a shop near the shop Hai Lu's grandfather had.

"Are you going to help your grandfather today?" Wing Loy asked.

"No," said Hai Lu, "today is a test for me; Grandfather will be gone and I will be alone in the shop. If I do well, Grandfather will let me work here every day of my vacation."

Wing Loy smiled and said, "I keep my father's shop all the time."

Hai Lu wanted to be more like his friend, because everyone said Wing Loy was a good salesperson. But Hai Lu was shy, and that made it hard for him to talk to strangers.

Most of the strangers were tourists, and they were bargain hunters who looked at everything.

Some people cheated the tourists by selling fake jade for real. When things like that happened, Hai Lu's grandfather got angry and said, "Soon tourists won't want to buy anything in Hong Kong."

"They'll always want to buy things from you, Grandfather," said Hai Lu.

Still, Hai Lu sometimes thought his grandfather took the truth too far. Sometimes customers would put a necklace down and not buy it when Grandfather told the truth: "That isn't real jade."

Hai Lu knew the customers would go to another store and there they would buy the same thing, but pay more for it.

Many times tourists could not tell real jade from fake.

Hai Lu asked his grandfather about it: "Wing Loy said that they don't know if they buy real or fake jade."

Grandfather looked at Hai Lu and said, "But we would know."

Today Hai Lu was going to do things another way. He would not lie, but if customers thought fake jade was real he would sell it to them.

Still, he felt nervous as he went into the store.

Hai Lu was still nervous when a tourist came in, but the woman, Ms. Carter, was nice. Hai Lu and Ms. Carter talked for a while, and soon she made Hai Lu feel good.

She picked up her favorite necklace and asked, "How much is this?"

Hai Lu told her.

"Oh, my," Ms. Carter said, "that's too much for me, even though I've always wanted a real jade necklace. Do you have any other necklaces to show me?"

Hai Lu didn't have a chance to say anything before Wing Loy ran in and said, "Hai Lu has many other necklaces."

Quickly Wing Loy pulled out some other necklaces which were fake jade. Still, Ms. Carter couldn't tell, so she picked one out, glad that it didn't cost so much.

"Wonderful," she said. "Now I'll have a real jade necklace."

Hai Lu began to feel bad as Ms. Carter began to pay for the necklace, but he tried to tell himself not to worry because she would never know. Then he remembered what Grandfather had said.

Suddenly Hai Lu said, "Wait! That isn't real jade!"

Angry, Wing Loy charged out of the store as Ms. Carter exclaimed, "Oh!" and put the box down.

But the kind Ms. Carter said, "Thank you. I'm sorry you have made your friend angry, but you were right to tell me the truth."

Still, Hai Lu wondered if he had been wrong because business had been bad and he had sold very little merchandise all day. Now his grandfather would think he was a bad salesperson.

The next morning, Hai Lu apologized: "I sold very little. I'm sorry."

Unworried, Grandfather said, "All days can't be good ones, but did you make any friends?"

Ms. Carter came in with her sister, just as Hai Lu said, "One, but I didn't sell her anything."

"Good morning," said Hai Lu. "This is my grandfather."

"You have a good grandson you can trust," said Ms. Carter.

She went on: "My sister can afford the very best quality, and she wants to buy a jade necklace."

Ms. Carter told her sister everything that had happened the day before, within the hearing range of Hai Lu's grandfather.

While Ms. Carter's sister was picking out a necklace, Ms. Carter's back was turned. Her sister whispered to Hai Lu, "Quickly, I want a necklace even better than this one to give to my sister as a present."

That way, Hai Lu sold two of the best necklaces in the store, and at the same time he knew that Ms. Carter would have a real jade necklace.

Hai Lu felt great, but he felt even better when his grandfather said, "Well, it looks like I found someone to help me during vacation — someone I can trust."

Think About This:

1. How did Hai Lu feel when his grandfather said he could trust him?
2. What would you have said to Ms. Carter when she was about to buy the necklace that she thought was real jade?

Sandra Simmons: Airline Pilot

When Sandra Simmons was a little girl playing in her yard, she would gaze into the sky and dream of flying through the clouds and across the sky. She would climb to the tops of the trees saying, "I want to be where the birds are."

She dreamed of growing up to be a pilot and flying airplanes through the high blue sky.

Some children's dreams fade as they grow up, but her dream remained with her into adulthood.

When she was old enough, Sandra went to pilots' school where she learned to fly airplanes. But that was not enough, because Sandra wanted to fly other people to places where they needed to go; she wanted to be an airline pilot.

There were no women flying the big jets for the airlines then; only men were allowed to be pilots. But Sandra changed that when she went to the special school for airline pilots and became one of the first woman airline pilots.

Sandra, a busy woman, lives in Texas but flies all over the United States as well as to other countries. She also teaches other people how to fly.

Sandra is the mother of two daughters, who are very proud of their mother. They say, "It's the greatest thing in the world. When other moms are sitting at home, our mom is way up in the air."

There is a woman who stays with Sandra's daughters when she is away flying.

According to Sandra, there are few difficulties. "I can be a pilot and a mother, too."

Sandra Simmons' dream of flying with the birds came true, and now she flies higher than any bird, and faster and farther.

Konrad Lorenz: Mother to Birds

Konrad Lorenz enjoys being outdoors where he can observe ducks and geese. He lives near a beautiful lake in Germany.

When he was a youth, Lorenz studied animals. He kept many kinds of pets including fish, birds, and even a monkey, but the animals had to be in cages. You see, Lorenz grew up in Vienna, and a big city apartment was no place for animals to be loose.

Later his family moved to a big house on the Danube River where Lorenz could allow his animals to be free, and he could see how some of them behaved outside.

Many times he relaxed by the river where once he watched a mother goose nest. He watched the baby geese hatch out of their eggs and look at their mother, who waited near them. They walked over to her, and from then on they followed her.

Lorenz recorded all the birds' actions, and he began to wonder why the baby geese followed their mother. No one taught them, so how did they know she was their mother?

When Lorenz grew up, he became a scientist and studied animals as his work. He continued to ask the same difficult questions. How did the baby geese know to follow their mother? "Perhaps they don't," Lorenz thought. "Perhaps they would follow anyone." To test his theory Lorenz did a strange thing.

He put goose eggs in an incubator, which is a box that keeps eggs warm. After the eggs hatched, Lorenz was the first object the geese saw. After that, the geese trailed him all over because they thought he was their mother.

Lorenz did the same thing over and over, and the geese always followed him, which

made Lorenz sure his theory was correct. To geese, whatever they see first is their mother.

Konrad Lorenz called this "imprinting," and imprinting ensures that baby geese are provided for. They will follow their mother to food, water, and rest.

Next, Lorenz tried the same theory with ducks, but it didn't work. He tried and tried, but the ducks ran away.

Then he thought that maybe ducks would follow only an object that quacked. Lorenz worked and worked, and soon he knew how to quack. When the ducks hatched, Lorenz was the first to quack at them, and the ducks followed, convincing Lorenz that imprinting happens in ducks, too.

Still, these ducks were a lot of trouble, because if Lorenz stopped quacking, they would cry. "Mother" had to make a special sound, and she couldn't be too tall.

So when he took his ducks for a walk, Lorenz had to squat and quack as he went, causing many people to stop and stare as they went by.

Since then, Lorenz has been "Mother" to many ducks and geese. You might see him in the morning when he goes for a swim. He is followed by a line of baby ducks or geese, and when he swims, they swim behind him.

Even when the baby geese grow up and have babies of their own, they run to greet Lorenz, because to them, he is still their mother.

Circus
Eleanor Farjeon

The brass band blares,
The naphtha flares,
The sawdust smells,
Showmen ring bells,
And oh! right into the circus-ring
Comes such a lovely, lovely thing,
A milk-white pony with flying tress,
And a beautiful lady,
A beautiful lady,
A *beautiful* lady in a pink dress!
The red-and-white clown
For joy tumbles down;
Like a pink rose
Round she goes
On her tip-toes
With the pony under —
And then, oh wonder!
The pony his milk-white tresses droops,
And the beautiful lady,
The beautiful lady,
Flies like a bird through the paper hoops!
The red-and-white clown for joy falls dead.
Then he waggles his feet and stands on his
    head,
And the little boys on the twopenny seats
Scream with laughter and suck their sweets.

Gelsey Kirkland

Dancing is an art that most people can appreciate and enjoy. When you hear music, you sometimes like to move your body with the rhythm and melody. Dancing is a natural way for you to show your feeling about music.

Ballet is a unique style of dancing that is made up of special kinds of movements that require strength as well as grace. Ballet dancers must learn to discipline their bodies at an early age. To be successful in their field, these dancers must train hard for many years.

The discipline that ballet requires is difficult to accomplish. Ballet requires a lot of work that often hurts, because the dancers must assume positions with their bodies that are not natural positions. These unique positions require practice, practice, and more practice.

Even if dancers become famous, their practice must never stop.

A female ballet dancer, called a ballerina, must learn to dance on her toes — right up on the very tips — and yet she must appear graceful when it is time for her to perform.

One ballerina, Gelsey Kirkland, began her ballet practice at a very early age, even before she started school. Once she began, she didn't want to stop. It was her dream to become a *prima ballerina*, and she would practice until her legs and feet hurt. Sometimes they hurt so much that she cried, but still she went on with her ballet exercises. That's the kind of discipline it takes to be a successful ballet dancer.

"One — two — three — four — "

Gelsey had to train for many hours in the studio to make her body assume the unique but graceful positions needed for ballet — the stretching, the jumping, and the dancing on her toes. Through the years Gelsey was able to develop great strength and grace, and her movements became beautiful to see. Her legs were very strong, and she would appear to fly to music like a graceful bird.

Gelsey didn't know it at this time, but she was going to accomplish her dream. She was going to become one of the greatest ballet dancers in the world. "One — two — three — four — "

Still the hours of stretching and jumping exercises plodded by. Then, when she was only fifteen years old, Gelsey was asked to perform with the New York City Ballet. After that, she became a star very quickly.

At last Gelsey could really appreciate the value of her many hours of practice. She decided that more practice could only make her more successful in her career. "One — two — three — four — "

Although practicing in the studio and stretching her legs in exercises was lonely work, Gelsey let nothing come between her and her art. It was as though she could see the value of nothing in life but

ballet, and she wanted only to be a part of it. Gelsey never stopped working and believing in herself. "One — two — three — four — "

Still she went through her exercises.

At the age of twenty-five — a young age to be such a successful dancer — Gelsey became the *prima ballerina* of the American Ballet Theater.

Although ballet is not as well known in America as it is in other parts of the world, more and more people are learning to appreciate and enjoy this unique and graceful art. People in the ballet world believe that the great young star, Gelsey Kirkland will help bring ballet into many more American lives.

"One — two — three — four — "

Even today Gelsey practices and does her exercises, and she looks ahead to becoming even more successful.

Do you have what it takes to assume a difficult career like ballet? If the career is something you enjoy and believe in, as Gelsey Kirkland believes in ballet, then you can do it.

Old-Time America: The Cattle Drive

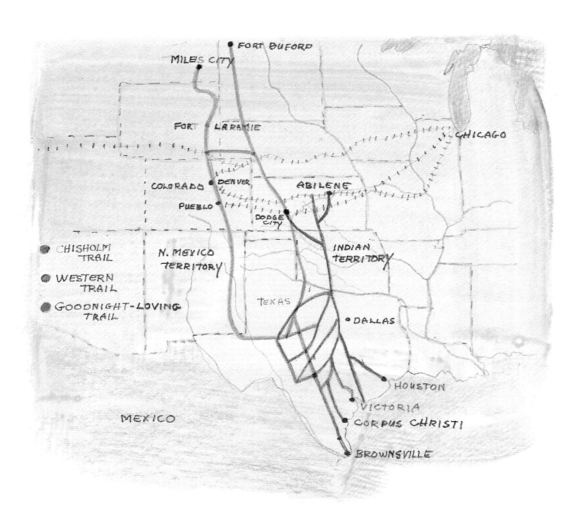

The time of the cattle drives north from Texas lasted twenty-five years, beginning in the 1860s and continuing into the 1880s. There were three trails — the Chisholm, the Western, and the Goodnight-Loving. A drive usually took from two to three months, with a crew of eleven hands herding about 2,500 cattle.

Sometimes the boss of the cattle drive owned the cattle, and sometimes he was just a ranch foreman. In any event, the boss's word was law on the drive.

There were eight cowhands on a drive, and all of them had different jobs. The two best cowhands rode point, at the head of the herd, where they guided the cattle in the right direction.

Four of the hands rode swing — in other words, at the side of the herd — where they kept the stragglers from straying too far.

Two of the newer hands rode drag, at the back of the herd, and kept the back of the herd moving.

All eight hands took turns in pairs on the night watch. They knew when to call the other hands to come relieve them by telling time by the stars.

The wrangler had a very difficult job, that of looking after a herd of half-wild horses. In addition to taking care of the horses, the wrangler also had to help the cook, who frequently was too old to ride.

The cook made meals at all hours, in all kinds of weather.

Driving the chuck wagon in front of the herd, he was first to arrive and set up camp each night. On his wagon were food, medicine, dishes, pots, and pans.

The drive often was treacherous for both the hands and the herd, since there could be stampedes, storms, floods, and sickness at any time.

After much hard work the drive was over, and the boss sold the cattle and paid his hands. The work had been worth it, because cattle that cost $5 in Texas were worth $40 to $50 in the North.

Think About This:

1. Why did people herd their cattle from Texas to the North?
2. Would you like the job of the wrangler? Why or why not?

More about Cowboys

There haven't always been cows and horses in America. It wasn't until Columbus landed here that cows set foot in America. And until the Spanish explorers came, there had been no horses. After the arrival of these animals came one of the best known figures in American history: the cowboy.

The first cowboys were Indian slaves in Mexico. Their Spanish masters called them *vaqueros* (Spanish for "cowboys"). The vaqueros were brought north when the

Spaniards came into California and New Mexico. They looked after the herds of cattle and horses owned by the Spaniards.

The American cowboy showed up much later. But just about everything the cowboys did or said or wore came from the Mexican vaqueros.

The wide-brimmed hats, or *sombreros*, and the coverings for the legs, or *chaps*, all came from the vaqueros.

The cowboys' saddles came from the Spaniards, and their talk was filled with Spanish words, such as *rodeo*, *corral*, and *bronco*.

The first American cowboys came to Texas after the war with Mexico. The only cattle were the wild and dangerous longhorns, and the American cowboys learned to herd and rope them from the vaqueros.

As the West was settled, the cattle and cowboys moved north. With songs and stories that grew up around them, the cowboys came to mean the American West itself.

But as American as cowboys seem to us, they owe what they are to the Spanish conquerors and the vaqueros of Mexico.

Through a Kaleidoscope

Marie Curie

Long ago in Poland, there lived a girl named Manya, who laughed and sang with her three sisters and a brother. Manya's father was a teacher and her mother a musician, and although they encouraged all their children to do excellent school work, nobody could know then just how famous little Manya would grow up to be.

Manya studied hard in her school and became a teacher of poor children in Poland who had no schools. But Manya was curious about many things, and she wanted to learn more. She went to a famous school in France, the Sorbonne, to learn how and why things do what they do. It was her ambition to be a scientist at a time when few women were encouraged to study.

While in Paris, Manya began spelling her name as they do in France — Marie. Marie met another energetic young scientist whose name was Pierre Curie. Both Pierre and Marie were devoted to science, and they found they had a great love for each other as well, so they were married.

Some scientists had just discovered some mysterious new rays called x-rays, and this news made Pierre and Marie very curious. It was not known what could be done with the x-rays, so one day Marie told Pierre, "I'd like to discover the secret of these strange rays."

To carry out her ambition, Marie first had to find a laboratory, a place where she could work. Pierre and Marie were poor, and to find the secrets of these rays would take a lot of money.

A school encouraged Marie by giving her a room for her laboratory. It was a gloomy, wet room, but it would do for Marie, and she began to work.

Marie was looking for the secrets of an element that had been found in the ground. It was slow work, and time plodded by, but the dedicated young scientist was getting closer and closer to an important discovery.

Pierre realized this and encouraged her in her work, and together they studied in the laboratory for many months. They finally discovered the element that was the source of the rays, and they named the element *radium*; they also gave a name to the rays — radioactivity. But they still couldn't find out exactly what the mysterious substance looked like.

It was very important work the two scientists were doing, but they had little money to go on. It was cold in the laboratory, and the place would fill with bad gases. Marie's hands had sores and burns, and Pierre became ill. They didn't know then that radioactivity is deadly; it can make people ill and can even kill them.

After four years Marie and Pierre discovered the secret they had set out to learn. On a dark evening in 1902, Marie and Pierre stood in their laboratory and saw a blue glow from their radium. It was there before them; they had found the mysterious secret of the rays at last! This was an important discovery for the world.

News reporters were at their door, and all kinds of people wanted to see them — scientists, doctors, teachers, and kings. The Curies were very famous now, and they were

given the great prize for science, the Nobel Prize. Marie was the first woman to win this prize, and the Curies were encouraged in their work by more gifts of money.

The two scientists wanted to get back to their laboratory to begin new work, but by this time Pierre and Marie had an energetic family. They were devoted to their two little girls, Irene and Eve, who kept them busy but happy.

Then during a rain storm in 1906, Pierre Curie was killed in a terrible street accident. Marie was discouraged because she was now alone with a family and important work still before her. She went back to the laboratory and began again. The work was even harder than before, but Marie made still more discoveries about radioactivity. One thing she learned was that these rays had hurt her greatly. Her hands were no better; they still had the mysterious sores and burns on them.

In 1911 the Nobel Prize came to Marie once more, making her famous as the first person to win the prize twice.

Not long after that, war came, and the energetic scientist wanted to help the wounded. By then doctors knew how to use the deadly source in a good way, to look into the body, so Marie had an x-ray machine made that could be taken to where wounded men were. Marie herself made a lot of trips with the x-ray machine, which helped save many lives.

At last the war came to an end, and Marie went once more to her laboratory. She had to have more of the element radium for her work, but it would cost much money.

When some women in America heard of her new ambition, they encouraged her with a gift of radium. To get the radium, Marie made a trip to America, where she met the President and many famous scientists and teachers.

When she went back to France, she found that everyone wanted to see her. Marie tried to see them all because she was very kind, but it was in her laboratory that she felt best, happy in her work.

In 1934, Marie became quite ill and had to stop her work. The doctors couldn't find out why Marie was so ill, and she became worse and died.

Later, scientists discovered that it was deadly radioactivity that put an end to Marie Curie's life.

Marie had made an important discovery, because now doctors studied the body with x-ray pictures and helped ill and injured people more.

Marie gave people another important discovery, as well. Up to that time many people didn't think that women could be scientists, but Marie Curie changed the way they felt. She was a dedicated scientist and a great woman.

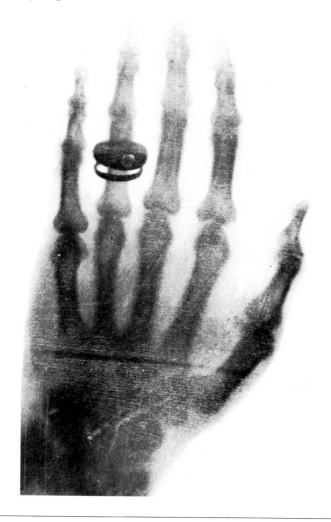

Where the Bear Went over the Mountain

As Judy reached for the matches above the fieldstone fireplace of the log cabin where she and her family had just moved, a letter fluttered to the floor. Her brother Stan got to it first and said, "I want the German stamp."

"O.K.," said Judy, "but what's written in the letter?"

Stan removed some yellow paper from the envelope and read the letter out loud:

> Dear Jim,
>
> When I first came to Germany, I did not intend to stay, but I've changed my mind. I concealed all the Indian artifacts in the cave where I found them, and I put the artifacts from the gold-rush days with them. Thought they'd be safe there until you moved into the cabin.
>
> Now, if you intend to open a store, the artifacts are all yours, or if not, just leave them. If someone can locate the cave "where the bear went over the mountain," well, finders keepers.
>
> Yours, Bill

"I'd really enjoy having those gold-rush things, if we can find them," Stan remarked.

"But that was years ago," said Judy. "I bet that man Jim found them."

"Maybe," said Stan, "but we could look."

"But how do we find 'where the bear went over the mountain'?" asked Judy.

"I don't know," said Stan, "but possibly Dad can examine the letter and help us."

They showed the letter to their father; however, he just put the letter back into the envelope and shook his head, remarking, "This isn't bear country, so I don't know what this letter means."

Stan and Judy thought Mr. Curry would possibly know about Jim and the cave, so they went to search for him. In a few minutes they were in the old man's log cabin, waiting anxiously for his opinion. After he'd read the letter, he said, "Although your dad is right, in my opinion the story is true, and I remember Jim. He talked about opening a store, but one day he just left, and I never saw him again."

"Maybe we ought to begin searching for a cave," said Judy.

"Before you do," said Mr. Curry, "would you bring me some firewood? There's a pile of logs up the road, and you can fill your sacks with them."

Judy and Stan went to the firewood pile and began to fill the sacks. The sun was setting when Judy glanced up from her work.

Suddenly she shouted, "Look!"

"What's the matter?" asked Stan.

Judy pointed to a cluster of low mountains. When Stan looked, his eyes got big with surprise.

One of the low mountains had some unusual rocks on it and, as the sun set, it cast a shadow against another, larger mountain. The shadow looked like it was moving over the larger mountain.

"It looks like — a bear!" Stan shouted.

"What do you know about that!" said Judy.

"It's our bear," Stan said, "and tomorrow morning we ought to hike up the mountain and locate that cave. We'll know right where to search for it."

Both children arose early the next morning and dressed rapidly. They went to the low mountain and hiked up the mountain toward the unusual rocks. When they finally reached the rock that had cast the shadow of the bear, Stan shook his head, saying, "Although this is the place, it doesn't look as if there's a cave around here."

Judy moved aside some bushes and crawled around a big rock. When she was safe on the other side, she pushed aside the rock, which hurtled down the mountain.

She suddenly pointed to where the rock had been and said, "It concealed the opening of the cave."

They both peered excitedly into the cave, and Stan shouted, "There it is!" He pointed at two big black boxes.

Stan and Judy dragged the boxes from the cave, and then they dragged them home.

They opened the boxes and found the Indian and gold-rush artifacts Bill had written about. At the bottom of one box Judy found a small leather bag and asked, "What's this?"

Stan glanced up and said, "That's a leather bag made to hold gold nuggets."

Judy examined the bag, turned it over, and poured several rust-brown rocks into her hand. Gold spots dotted the rocks. "They're gold nuggets!" shouted Judy.

"And to think," Stan said, "we didn't know if we'd enjoy being here on the mountain."

Gordon Parks

Sometimes people go through life never seeing the many possibilities for success in the world and, too often, they don't see the possibilities in themselves. But those possibilities are there in everyone, and it is important that we be aware of talents within us and make them flower in the world.

This is not always easy, and sometimes it seems everything works against it.

Gordon Parks is an artist who found it difficult to bring his talents to life. Almost everything in Parks's early life said, "You're poor and black. There's nothing for you but this, so forget it."

But Gordon Parks refused to believe the message, because there was a small flame in him that burned with poetry and art.

The flame grew as Gordon grew, until the whole world became aware of his talents.

Gordon Parks was born on a farm in Kansas in 1912, the youngest of fifteen children. Although the Parks family was very poor, their house was full of love. Gordon's mother was strong, and she made Gordon and her other children aware of their sense of worth. Gordon recalls, "She gave me ambition and purpose, and she set the course I have traveled. I didn't know what lay ahead of me, but I believed in myself."

When Gordon was sixteen years old his mother died, and he left Kansas to live with his sister. Her husband didn't like Gordon, though, and forced him to leave.

Gordon was now alone on the gloomy, ghetto streets of

Saint Paul with nowhere to go, nowhere to sleep. Unemployed and discouraged, he was hungry, cold, and alone that freezing winter. Then his father and sisters came to Saint Paul, and everyone was together.

While Gordon went to high school, he was forced to work at night. Even though work was hard to find, everyone at the Parks's house had to work because they were so poor. People all over the country were unemployed, and black people had the hardest time of all finding work.

Sometimes things were so difficult for Gordon, he thought of robbing someone. Once when he was unemployed he pulled a knife on a streetcar conductor. The conductor glared at Gordon and the knife, and Gordon started to shake. He thought of all his mother had taught him about right and wrong, and he said, "Conductor, would you give me a dollar for this knife? I'm hungry and have no place to stay."

The conductor said he would give him two dollars and Gordon could keep his knife, but Gordon said "No," and jumped from the streetcar. He felt so ashamed and frightened that he ran away.

Gordon was so poor he was forced to drop out of school, but he often went to the library to read, study, and learn. Although he could not read music, Gordon began writing many songs, mostly very sad songs and the blues.

Gordon began working very fast and hard. He painted pictures, wrote poetry, and played basketball.

It was too much, and one day Gordon fell over, sick. Just like that, he crashed to the floor and was taken to a hospital. He was very, very sick, and he had to stay in bed for six months.

Gordon realized from this that he had been doing too much, and he said, "I'll have to take my time from now on. I'll have to take the things slowly that were meant to be slow."

He got better and soon he was working in a hotel.

As time went on, Gordon found himself working on a train. One day he was looking at some photos in a magazine. They were very good photos and, as Gordon looked more closely at them, he realized they were done by artists who were photographers. Gordon decided right then he wanted to see and know more about photography.

"Suddenly I saw all the things I could say in photographs, and I made up my mind to become a professional photographer," recalls Gordon.

Gordon bought a camera right away and began taking photos, and in a short time people began to be aware of him and his work.

A camera store thought his photos were so good they put them in their window.

When Gordon's photos of beautiful young black women were printed on the front pages of some newspapers, a women's fashion store in Saint Paul had Gordon start making photos of their clothes. Gordon began making money in fashion photography, and he was beginning to feel like a professional. People all over town were wanting Gordon to take photos for them.

One lady of fashion who gave Gordon a lot of help was Marva Louis, wife of the famous boxing champion, Joe Louis. Marva Louis helped Gordon get a place where he could work on his photos, and she helped him meet a lot of well-known people.

Gordon made his money taking photos of rich people of fashion, but he realized his eyes and heart were elsewhere.

He took the money he made and bought more film. He

wanted to make photos of what he saw in the ghetto, so he went back to the gloomy streets where poor people lived.

He turned his camera on the faces in the ghetto, the faces of people hurt and lost, and faces looking for a way out. Some faces held pride and courage, and some faces held anger, but all were important faces.

Gordon felt all the hard, lost, hurt feelings in those faces because he had been there. He knew all the world should see those faces, and as he worked harder he captured those faces in photos.

Those pictures were shown in a Saint Paul art center, and many people came to see them. Then Gordon was given a special prize of money so that he wouldn't have to do anything but take photos of whatever he wanted. As an artist he was happier than he had ever been, doing what he knew best, and doing it with some freedom.

Later, in 1949, Gordon Parks began doing special reports and photos for *Life* magazine. For over twenty years Gordon did photos for the magazine, and people all over the world began to know his name and his works.

Gordon brought back photos of ways of life many people never see. Many of his reports for the magazine were stories of black lives; some of these people were famous, but many were not. Their faces, captured in Gordon's photos, came into homes all over the country and told their stories.

Another time, Gordon took photos that shared with all the world his feelings about his favorite poetry. Gordon always hoped that his photos could show something not seen before and help tired eyes to see again.

Later, in 1962, Parks went to work in Hollywood, making television films about life in the black ghetto. Although Gordon had wanted to make feature films for a long time, he found that this was difficult to do. Some people in the film business made it hard for black men and women to work.

But, as he had all his life, Gordon Parks kept working until he broke through.

His first Hollywood movie was *The Learning Tree,* made from a book Gordon had written in 1963. The book was about a young black boy growing up in Kansas. Gordon was in complete charge of the movie. He also wrote the music for the film.

When the film came out and people saw it, everyone realized Gordon Parks was a good film-maker. It seemed there was little Gordon Parks could not do.

He would say, "I have been able to turn all the bad feelings inside me to work. Maybe that's the reason I have done so many things. When I felt I couldn't say what was inside of me in my photography, I turned to poetry or music or a book."

Through all the hurt and hunger, Gordon Parks kept his flame of talent burning, and it burned so brightly all the people in the world could see themselves better.

Think About This:

1. Why do you think Gordon Parks was able to escape the ghetto while others were not?
2. Gordon Parks saw the possibilities in his life and in himself and made them flower. What possibilities do you see in your life?

My Mother Saw a Dancing Bear

Charles Causley

My mother saw a dancing bear
By the schoolyard, a day in June.
The keeper stood with chain and bar
And whistle-pipe, and played a tune.

And bruin lifted up its head
And lifted up its dusty feet,
And all the children laughed to see
It caper in the summer heat.

They watched as for the Queen it died.
They watched it march. They watched it halt.
They heard the keeper as he cried,
'Now, roly-poly!' 'Somersault!'

And then, my mother said, there came
The keeper with a begging-cup,
The bear with burning coat of fur,
Shaming the laughter to a step.

They paid a penny for the dance,
But what they saw was not the show;
Only, in bruin's aching eyes,
Far distant forests, and the snow.

Rumpelstiltskin

CAST:

Miller   First Soldier

Elsa   Second Soldier

King   Storyteller

Dwarf

Scene 1

Storyteller: Once upon a time there lived a poor miller who had a beautiful little daughter, and as she grew older, he wondered how he would find a good husband for her. One day he said to his daughter,

Miller: I am beginning to worry about you, Elsa, my child.

Elsa: Why should you worry, Father?

Miller: It is time for you to marry, but I have no money to give you a dowry.

Elsa: Then who will marry me, except a man as poor as we are?

Miller: You have no money, but you are an unusually beautiful girl — beautiful enough to be a queen.

Elsa: (Laughs) Oh, Father, are you sure I could really be a queen?

Miller: (Thoughtful) Yes, you could be a queen if only the king could see you!

Elsa: How could I ever get in sight of the king?

Miller: If he ever saw you, Elsa, I'm sure he would wish to make you his queen, but how can I make that happen? Ah, I think I have an idea!

Elsa: What is it, Father?

Miller: I must tell it to the king first, so go on with your spinning while I think it out.

Storyteller: The next day the miller and his daughter went to the king's palace, where a soldier stopped them at the gate.

First Soldier: Halt! Who goes there?

Miller: A miller and his daughter, soldier. We live in a cottage down by the river.

First Soldier: What would a miller and his daughter want with the king? Go to the kitchen if you want to sell your flour and bread to the king.

Miller: I must see the king himself, for I want to do him a favor. Let me pass, if you please.

First Soldier: You, a poor miller, want to do the king a favor?

Miller: Yes. You see, my daughter has many talents besides being beautiful. She can bake the best pumpernickel bread, and she can spin straw into gold.

Elsa: Father, what are you saying?

First Soldier: Now, that is a real favor and something the king would really like to see. He always needs gold to make him wealthy. You may go into the throne room, but your daughter must wait out here till the king sends for her.

Sound: (Door opens and shuts.)

King: Well, who are you, and what do you want?

Miller: Your Majesty, I am a humble flour miller and I have a beautiful daughter. I have brought you a loaf of her best pumpernickel bread.

King: There are many beautiful girls here and they all can bake quite well.

Miller: My daughter is not only beautiful and can bake, she can do something fantastic. She can spin straw into gold!

King: Well, that is something fantastic. I always need gold and more gold to make me wealthy, but it sounds impossible.

King: (Takes a bite of the bread) Straw into gold! Bring her here this afternoon, and we will see if she can spin as well as she bakes pumpernickel bread.

Miller: Your Majesty, my daughter is waiting outside this room.

King: So much the better! Soldier, take the miller's daughter into one of the rooms with a spinning wheel and see that the room is filled with straw.

Miller: Wouldn't you like to watch my beautiful daughter as she spins, Your Majesty?

King: No. Now go, miller, and tell your daughter that if she does not spin all the straw into gold by morning, she shall be thrown into the dungeon for the remainder of her life.

Miller: Your Majesty, but —

King: Go, I said. Soldier, see that the girl is locked in the room all night.

Storyteller: Elsa, the flour miller's daughter, was locked in the room full of straw and told to spin the straw into gold by morning or die in the dungeon. Poor Elsa didn't know what to do.

Elsa: Oh, what shall I do?

Dwarf: (Cross, gruff voice) Good afternoon, miller's daughter.

Elsa: Where did you come from, little man?

Dwarf: I came through the keyhole. Why are you crying, miller's daughter?

Elsa: The king has ordered me to spin all this straw into gold by morning or I will die in the dungeon, and I don't even spin wool very well.

Dwarf: What will you give me if I spin it into gold for you?

Elsa: I have very little of value, but I'll give you my velvet hair ribbon if you can spin it for me.

Dwarf: All right, then it's a bargain; so let me sit down at the spinning wheel.

Scene 2

Storyteller: The little man spun and spun until all the straw was gone and all the spools were full of gold. Then he was gone as quickly as he had come. Early the next morning the king came.

Sound: (Door opens.)

King: Gold! So you really can spin straw into gold. This is truly fantastic.

Elsa: You see the gold before you, Your Majesty.

King: Lovely, shining gold, and I will be wealthy. Now, miller's daughter, you shall be put into a larger room full of straw, and you will spin it into gold before morning, if you value your life.

Elsa: But, Your Majesty —

King: Soldier, have a larger room filled with straw and take the spinning wheel and the girl into it.

Storyteller: So Elsa was taken into a much larger room which was filled with mounds of straw for her to change into gold. She looked at the straw and spools, and sighed.

Dwarf: Good day, miller's daughter.

Elsa: The little man again! I'm so glad to see you! Please, will you help me again today?

Dwarf: Tell me first, what will you give me if I spin this straw into gold?

Elsa: I will give you the only item of value I have left and that is the gold ring from my finger.

Dwarf: Very well! Give me the ring; and now let me sit at your spinning wheel.

Storyteller: The next day, when the king came to the room, he looked at the spools of gold and smiled. This time he looked at the miller's daughter, too, and he saw that she was beautiful, but he wanted still more gold. He led her into an even larger room filled with straw.

King: I command that you spin for me one night more, miller's daughter.

Elsa: But, Your Majesty, I cannot.

King: Why not? You have done it twice, and now do you refuse to do it again?

Elsa: Oh, no, Your Majesty, but —

King: If it is all spun by sunrise, you shall become my queen, and you will be as rich as I am.

Elsa: How can I —

King: How can you, a poor flour miller's daughter, marry a king? Why, you can spin more gold than any princess ever has, and now, not another word. I ask this one last favor, so set to work and make your king wealthy.

Elsa: Oh, dear, if only the little man would come again; but I have nothing of value to give him.

Scene 3

Storyteller: Elsa was left with the command to do twice the work of her two previous nights for the king, and she still could not spin a single piece of straw into gold. Will the dwarf come again to help her?

Dwarf: Well, here we are again, miller's daughter, and you're still in trouble.

Elsa: Oh! Thank goodness you've come to me again! Please, will you spin for me this third time?

Dwarf: What will you offer me this time?

Elsa: I have given you everything I have of value, so there is nothing left to give you.

Dwarf: There is one thing for which I will spin tonight.

Elsa: What is that?

Dwarf: As payment you must promise that when you are queen, you will give me your first child.

Elsa: Oh, no, I beg you, anything — my crown, my jewels, but not my baby. *(Pause)* But then, who knows if I shall ever become queen? Very well, little man, I agree; I promise that if I become queen you shall have my first child.

Dwarf: That's what I want! Now I'll sit down and spin.

Storyteller: Early the next morning the king came again and found the room full of spools of gold.

King: Excellent, more gold! How the room shines with its light!

Elsa: Your Majesty is pleased!

King: I am, for it is more gold than I ever expected, and I shall keep my promise. You shall be my queen, and I will never command you to spin again.

Elsa: Oh, Your Majesty!

King: Now that I look at you well, I see that you are really as beautiful as your father said.

Elsa: Thank you, Your Majesty. I shall try to be a good queen.

King: I shall call for the ladies of the palace to dress you in the finest gowns, and today will be our wedding day.

Scene 4

Storyteller: So the flour miller's daughter and the king were married, and they were very happy. About a year later, when the queen had a beautiful little son, she had forgotten all about the little man and her promise to him. But one night, as she sat with her baby in her arms, the little man came into her room.

Dwarf: Good evening, Queen.

Elsa: Oh! The little man who helped me spin the straw into gold.

Dwarf: Yes, indeed. Now you must keep your promise and give me your child.

Elsa: Oh, no, no, I can't give him up!

Dwarf: But you promised, and a bargain is a bargain.

Elsa: Oh, I know I promised. But it was to save my life. Oh, please, kind little man, I'll give you anything else you say — gold, jewels, my crown, anything — but not my baby! I love him so!

Dwarf: Impossible, nothing else will do. *(Pause)* Well, maybe one last chance, because all I really want is my just payment. I'll give you three days to find out my name and if you do that, you shall keep your child, and you will bake bread for me everyday. If you don't guess my name, you must give me your son and all the gold I have spun, and your crown, and your jewels, and everything else you have of value.

Elsa: Oh, thank you, little man, for this one last favor, and I'll try to guess your name.

Dwarf: *(Strange laugh)* You'll have to try very, very hard, for it is nearly impossible.

Storyteller: The queen did not want to humble herself by telling the king about the little man. She lay awake all night thinking of all the names she had ever heard. When the little man came again the next night, he found the queen sitting in a mound of paper with thousands of names printed on it. She spent the whole night reading the names, and the gruff little man's answer was "No" to each. The next day the queen sent soldiers out to learn all the strange names that they could, and when night came, she waited for the dwarf.

Dwarf: Well, Queen, do you think you know my name now?

Elsa: Is your name Shorty?

Dwarf: No, it is not.

Elsa: Is your name Spindleshanks or Crosspatch?

Dwarf: No, I'm not called any of these, and you have one night left to try to guess my name. If you can't guess it then, I shall have your child, your crown, your jewels, and your gold, and you will again be humble and poor.

Storyteller: The queen was very worried that third day, as her task seemed more and more impossible. Each soldier came back with mounds of names, but no new names. Then the last soldier came and asked to see the queen, and he told a strange story.

Second Soldier: Your Majesty, I saw a very strange sight today.

Elsa: Will it help me guess the little man's name?

Second Soldier: Perhaps. I was coming through a dense, deep, dark forest when I came to a tiny house. I walked quietly to a crack in the wall and looked in, and hopping up and down before a huge fire was a strange little man. As he hopped he said,

> "Today I brew, tomorrow I bake,
> Next morning I the queen's child take.
> How glad I am she does not know
> My name is Rumpelstiltskin! Ho!"

Elsa: That must be the dwarf! Thank you for your good news, and take this piece of gold as a payment.

Second Soldier: Thank you, Your Majesty.

Storyteller: Soon after the soldier was gone, the little man came into the queen's room again and reminded her that this was her last night.

Dwarf: Well, Queen, I command you to tell me my name!

Elsa: Are you called Conrad or James?

Dwarf: No, and now your wealth and child are mine.

Elsa: (Smiling) Not just yet, for the night is not over and I have one name left — Rumpelstiltskin!

Dwarf: (Angry) The fairies must have told you! The fairies must have told you! *(He stamps his foot.)*

Elsa: Now you can't take my baby, and you can't take any of my wealth. Go ahead and stamp your foot as hard as you like! You have stamped your foot into the ground, and it is impossible to pull it out!

Dwarf: (He stamps his other foot.)

Elsa: Now your other foot is deep in the ground, and you are sinking!

Storyteller: Yes, the little man sank down into the ground and was never seen again. The queen kept her baby and her crown and her jewels, but everyday she baked two loaves of pumpernickel bread — one for the king and one that always disappeared as it sat cooling in the palace kitchen window.

WAVES

There's big waves and little waves,
   Green waves and blue,
Waves you can jump over,
   Waves you dive through,
Waves that rise up
   Like a great water wall,
Waves that swell softly
   And don't break at all,
Waves that can whisper,
   Waves that can roar,
And tiny waves that run at you
   Running on the shore.

By Eleanor Farjeon

How You Play the Game

Make a Racing Car

Part of the fun of playing a game is constructing some of the toys you will be playing with. Try constructing racing cars with some empty spools.

You'll need some large wooden spools, some rubber bands, a few lollipop sticks, some carpet tacks, and the flat kind of washers. Locate a hammer, and you are ready to begin.

Hammer one of the tacks into one end of the spool. Allow the head of the tack to stick out just a little bit.

Put a rubber band through the hole in the spool and loop one end of the rubber band around the tack. The rubber band should be sticking out at the other end of the spool.

If it's too long, you can tie a knot in it to make it shorter.

Put one of the washers over the rubber band at the end of the spool that is not held by the tack. Put the lollipop stick 2.54 centimeters (about one inch) through the rubber band loop.

Hold the spool in one hand, wind up the stick, then carefully put the car on the floor and point it in the direction you want it to go. Now release the car!

The spool should shoot straight across the floor. If it doesn't, wind up the stick again, a little less or a little more. Locate a different rubber band and try that. When it goes as fast as you'd like and in the direction you point it, the car is ready to race.

Help your friends make their own cars. Then you can have races to see which car will be the champion.

Paint a different numeral on each car so that you can tell whose car is ahead.

Hot Rod Racers: You and a friend can have a hot rod race. You will need to have on hand two empty spools, two large beads, cardboard, and some strong string or cord.

Paint each spool a different color. Next, cut circles for the wheels out of cardboard. They should all be the same size — about the size of a dime if the spools are small, or the size of a quarter if the spools are large.

Use a black pen to draw tires and spokes on the wheels.

Paint a numeral on the front and back of each spool. Allow the paint to dry, then use tacks to put two wheels on each side of the spools. Use four wheels for each spool.

Your hot rod spool cars are now ready to race. Your next project can be building the racetrack for the cars.

Cut a piece of cord as long as you are tall. Run the cord through the hole in one of the beads and make a knot at each end. Now that the bead can't slip down the cord, run the other end of the cord through the hole in the spool car and tie the end of the cord to the bottom of a table leg. Do the same thing with the other spool car, but this time tie the cord to another table leg. Consider which car will be your favorite.

To race the cars, hold the bead end of the cord and pull the cord very tight. Move away from the table a little so that you allow the cord to be on a slant.

Holding the cord waist-high, start the car at the bead end by gently wiggling the cord. Simultaneously, your friend will do the same thing with the other car. Both cars will be traveling in the same direction. The first car to get to the table leg is the champion.

The Season

"It's baseball season, again," Amy sighed, trying to sound as if she didn't really care.

"I know," said her mother, as if she didn't believe that Amy didn't really care.

"Maybe the coach will let me play this year," Amy said, as she shrugged and studied her shoes.

"You've worked hard this year, and your muscles are better, so maybe he will," said Mom, smiling. "Chin up and good luck, Amy — if you really want to play on the team."

"I really do," said Amy, and she trotted to the closet to pick up her glove and cap.

"I'm going to practice, now," she called, and she shut the door with a thump.

When she arrived at the baseball park, a lot of boys were there with the coach. An old bag full of bats and some new white balls and some old dirty ones lay in the dust. Everyone just stood around, not talking and trying not to look nervous.

At last they all went over to stand by first base, and Amy followed them slowly. The coach called the first two boys to be batter and catcher. He scattered everyone else around the field, and he pitched. After some practice swings, the batter missed the first two balls, taking such hard swings that he almost went into a spin.

"Get your left elbow up and take it easy," was the advice of the coach.

The batter hit the next ball straight at Amy, who put up her glove, catching the ball with a neat thump.

"Nice catch," someone called, and Amy said, "Thanks."

The two boys rotated positions, and the one who had been catching hit a long ball to right field. Then everyone rotated again, so they would all have a chance to play all the other positions.

Amy couldn't wait for her turn at bat, because she knew she could hit, and her brother Jim knew she could hit, too. She had "good wrists," he said, and she knew how to use them.

After everyone had rotated, the coach gave the thirsty team some water and talked about how everyone who came to practice could play in the games.

But Max — Amy knew him from school — glared at her in a disgusted way and said, "Is *she* going to play?"

"If she comes to practice all season, she can," said the coach, looking unhappy.

Max, one of the biggest boys in their class at school, had huge muscles and long legs, and he could really hit the ball. "If she is, I'm not," he warned, and he picked up his jacket, threw it over his shoulder, and walked away.

The coach shrugged and said, "Sorry about that."

Fred said, "Hey, coach, aren't you going to try to get him to come back? We really need him, because he'll probably hit four hundred this year."

"Sorry about that," the coach said again, "but it's up to him."

After that day the team had to practice every Saturday and Wednesday afternoon. They worked hard and their muscles hurt, but they all told jokes and laughed together as they got to know each other . . . Amy, too. She was good and she knew it, and they all knew it. She could play all positions as well as anyone else (better than most), and she could pitch like a professional.

When the day of the first real game came, though, she felt funny. She couldn't eat all her lunch, and she kept trying to get Mom and Jim to go to the car.

"We have almost all afternoon," grumbled Jim as he put on his jacket.

"I'm just nervous," sighed Amy, "and I want to get to the baseball park."

At last Mom, Jim, and Amy rode to the baseball park together. When they arrived, Jim gave her some last-minute advice: "Keep the ball low and tight, and never throw high and away to them."

"I know, I know," mumbled Amy as she scratched her elbow. "You've told me all that before."

She wished her head wouldn't spin around so much. When she got to the dugout and talked to Fred, he said, "Man, am I nervous!" When she heard him say that, Amy didn't feel so scared, but her legs still felt like water.

She warmed up by pitching to Fred, who was the catcher. When she took her place on the mound, the first batter she had to face was Max — the same Max who had walked off their team and who now played for the Hot Shots.

She was more nervous than ever, but her concentration was on the glove held by the catcher. She wound up and threw a pitch right by Max, and then another. The third pitch was high, for a ball, but Max fouled out on the next ball she threw, which was low and fast. The next batter fouled out, and the third one struck out.

"Great!" yelled the coach, giving her a clap on the back that almost bounced her over.

She put on the helmet, picked up some bats, and warmed up with some easy practice swings while Max warmed up to pitch. His first ball came right at her left elbow, but she jumped back just in time, and the umpire called, "Ball one!"

Max shrugged and threw again, this time straight at her chin, and she had to fall down to miss the ball.

"Ball two," called the umpire, and he glared at Max and warned him to take it easy.

After Amy got up and shook the dust off, Max pitched right down the middle and then laughed when, swinging so hard that her legs almost curled right out from under her, she missed the ball.

"You've got her scared now, Max," someone from the other team yelled.

Disgusted now, Amy pushed out her chin and blew some dust from her face, and she was ready. She wasn't scared; she would just have to bat better than Max could pitch.

When he wound up and threw again, Amy saw the ball coming right down the middle. She knew it was his fast ball, and her eyes never left it. She brought her wrists around, the bat followed, and her strong hands carried it. The fat part of the bat met the ball — she saw them meet in that second before she heard the sound of it. Crack!

And then the ball took off, and so did Amy. She threw down the bat and started to first base.

Everyone yelled "Run!" as the other team scattered, trying to see the ball in the sun. After she got to first base, Amy looked up, and she saw the ball going and going, getting smaller and smaller. It went straight over the glove of a fielder, over the fence, and into a car lot. As she touched second base, she heard it thump on the roof of a car. The fielder stood with his head down, looking disgusted, as Amy passed third base and ran to home plate.

Fred was there to clap her on the shoulder, and the smiling coach did, too, and all the rest of the team behind them. The field seemed to spin as she trotted straight into the dugout and plopped down. She looked around and found her mom, who was smiling from ear to ear, and her brother, who yelled, "Great hit!"

Then she looked out at Max where he stood all alone on the mound. He had to pitch to Fred now, but his concentration seemed to be gone. He needed the advice of a big brother — the ball was getting wild on him when he should have kept it low and tight.

She was going to keep the ball low and tight when it was *her* turn again, no matter what happened — no matter what, not just for the afternoon but all season long.

The Horse Who Went Fishing

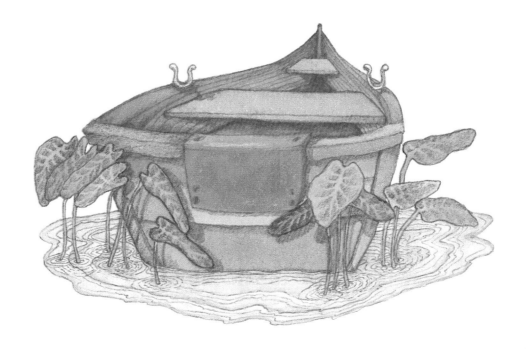

On the hill above the lake, the farmer and his horse were plowing back and forth across the bumpy field under the warm summer sun.

The farmer looked at the cool, inviting lake and thought about fishing.

"Work, work, nothing but work," said the disgusted farmer, looking down at his brightly painted rowboat, tied to the dock. "I really would like to go fishing, but naturally work comes first."

"On the other hand," said the farmer, looking at the shimmering lake, "there is definitely more than one kind of work. I plant seeds for food, and planting is work, so if fish is food, then fishing must certainly be work — and work comes first!"

"It will surely be cool on the lake," the farmer said, "and fried fish will definitely taste good for supper."

The tired horse looked up; he knew what supper was, but what was that about fishing? "I've never gone fishing," he said to himself, "and that rowboat looks too small for two, but I will surely have to go fishing if fishing is work because the farmer has never done any work without me."

The farmer led the horse to the lush meadow, then he hurried up to the house.

"I'm going fishing," he said to his wife.

"What about your lunch?" asked his wife.

"I can eat in the boat," said the eager farmer, "while I work."

"What about your afternoon nap?" asked his concerned wife.

"I can nap in the boat," said the farmer, "while I work."

"What about the baking sun?" asked his wife.

"My hat has a very wide brim," the farmer said thoughtfully.

"You certainly have no bait," said his wife.

"There are millions of snails in the garden," the farmer responded, "and they're eating up your lovely flowers."

"I shall pack you a nourishing lunch at once," said his wife.

The farmer went out and filled a pail with snails.

"Don't forget your lunch," reminded his wife. "Try to take a nap, and definitely wear your hat, and get rid of the snails, and —"

The impatient farmer took his sack lunch and his big-brimmed hat and the pail full of snails and hurried along the winding path past the meadow and down the hill to the lake.

"The good farmer wants me to rest; how kind of him," said the horse, as he watched the farmer go by. "But it's terribly hot in the meadow, and I'm tired of eating grass. Fish might taste good for supper. I'd better hurry," said the horse as he leaped over the fence and galloped down the hill onto the slippery dock. "The farmer is a kind man, but he can't do his work without me."

The farmer was already in the little fishing boat, stowing away his gear, and he didn't look up.

"The farmer will surely be glad to see me," said the horse as his foot slipped, and he slid off the end of the dock — SPLASH!

Waves rocked the little red rowboat.

"Who is rocking my boat?" said the farmer angrily as he turned, and into the water he went — SPLASH!

The shivering farmer bobbed to the surface and reached for the side of his rowboat, but the boat was not there.

"Who took my boat?" he said, wiping his eyes and looking around. "I see a small red boat out there, but it isn't mine because there's a horse sitting in it."

"Wait a minute!" he said, looking again. "It's not only my boat, it's also my horse! How could this happen to me; how could this happen to me?"

The boat drifted far out toward the middle of the lake.

"Come back!" the farmer shouted; "come back, back, back!"

The horse heard the farmer shouting and perked his ears.

"Sack, did he say 'sack'?" said the horse to himself as he looked around and saw the sack of lunch the farmer's wife had prepared.

"The farmer wants me to eat his lunch; how kind of him," the horse said, waving at the farmer to show he understood, and he took a big green pickle from the sack.

The boat drifted farther and farther away.

"Swim!" the farmer shouted. "You crazy horse; swim, swim, swim!"

"Brim," said the horse; "did he say 'brim'?" and he looked around and found the big hat.

"The farmer surely wants me to wear his hat; how kind of him," said the horse, and waved to show that he understood and put on the hat at once.

The farmer shouted as the boat drifted farther,
"Jump, jump, jump!"

"Dump," said the horse; "did he say 'dump'?" and
he looked around and found the pail of snails.

"The farmer wants me to have more room; how
kind of him," said the horse, and waved to show that he
understood and dumped the snails into the water, pail
and all.

"You are a fool, you crazy horse!" the farmer
shouted. "And so am I; no horse, no boat, no fish, no
pail, no lunch, no hat, no anything. We are fools, fools,
fools!" he cried, as he shook his fist at the horse and
made his way back to shore.

"The farmer has decided not to fish so he waved
good-by, and he hopes I am cool; how kind of him,"
said the horse. "I shall fish for both of us."

The horse took a bite of the pickle and said, "I hope
fish taste better than this." He leaned back in the boat
and shut his eyes, and the hat slid over his nose, and the
boat drifted on.

"If this is really fishing," said the horse, "I wonder
where the fish are?"

He didn't have long to wait, for the boat soon
drifted into the reeds and stopped. *Splash* — a fine,
shiny fish leaped high out of the water and stared at the
horse.

"Well, have you never seen a horse before?" said
the horse, sitting up.

"Certainly not eating pickles in a rowboat!" the
fish said, so surprised that he promptly flopped into the
boat and lay there gasping.

Splash — another fine fish leaped out of the water to stare at the horse.

"Have you never seen a horse before?"

"Not eating pickles and wearing a hat!" said the fish, dropping into the boat and flopping about.

When the horse saw the farmer swimming toward him with a rope he said, "How kind of him; he knows I'm tired of fishing."

The farmer tied the rope to the boat, and then he saw the fish. So he shut his eyes and when he opened them, the fish were still there. The farmer towed the boat to shore, led the horse back to the meadow, and took the fish up to the house.

"How wet and angry you look!" remarked his wife. "Fishing surely must be work, but did you get rid of all the snails?"

"No," said the grumpy farmer, "the horse did."

"That is no way to talk; you are angry because you're hungry and tired," said his wife. "Did you eat your lunch and take a nap in the boat?"

"No," said the farmer, "the horse ate my lunch and took my nap."

"The warm sun has made you angry," his wife said; "and did you wear your hat in the boat?"

"No," said the farmer, "the horse wore my hat in the boat."

"You are angry," said his wife, "but it doesn't matter since you caught two fine fish for our supper — and don't tell me the horse caught the fish!"

"But he did," said the farmer, "so I guess I just can't do my work without him."

Learn to Play Soccer

Soccer is fast becoming the most popular sport in the world. It's still way behind other sports in the United States, because it's not familiar. But it's becoming more popular every day. If you haven't ever played soccer but would like to be the first on your block to learn some soccer skills, just continue to read on.

Probably you are aware of some things about the game already. There are eleven players on a side. The players keep the ball moving by kicking and heading it. The goalie is permitted to use his hands. The goal is 24 feet wide and 8 feet high. If you weren't aware of these things, ask your teacher for a book that has information about the game of soccer or look in the library.

Here are the first steps to become familiar with in learning to play this exciting game. "We start young players by teaching them how to trap the ball," says Russell G. Simpson, who is the coach of a very successful soccer team in Vermont.

To trap the ball means to stop a pass or shot on goal and make the ball fall to your feet. Let the ball hit your thigh, chest, or instep and "give" as the ball hits. That means when the ball hits you, move your chest, thigh, or foot back. Did you ever throw a ball into something soft? This works the same way.

While a young player is learning the methods to kick, Coach Russell Simpson also shows the player three basic passes.

An instep kick is made when the leg snaps forward and the instep hits the ball hard.

A push pass is made when the inside of the foot hits the ball for a very short pass.

A flick is made when the outside of the foot hits the ball, usually during a dribble.

There are various other kicks as well, but the coach thinks these are the most significant. All of them are permitted as passes or as shots on goal, but the flick is not used often.

Once the basic skills have been mastered, it's time to put them into practice. Coach Simpson says to attempt a game of three against one in a 10-yard square. The three offensive players stand in an imaginary triangle and try to pass the ball to each other by instep kicks, push passes, and flick passes. The one defensive player takes away the ball if the player is able to do so.

After a while, the offensive players attempt to move the ball downfield. They try to stay within an imaginary square.

"Through this drill, players learn ball control and get an idea of the game," the coach says. "In a real game we try to have triangles around the ball all the time as we move the ball downfield."

Suppose you're in a triangle drill — or better yet, a real game. The ball comes at your stomach and you lift your knee, the ball hits against the inside of your thigh and drops at your feet. You take a quick shot at the left side of the goal.

The goalie of the opposing team jumps to the side of the goal, grabs the ball, and brings it to his stomach as he falls. Save! The goalie jumps up, throwing the ball downfield. Bad pass! Your teammate snaps her neck and hits the ball, heading it toward you, and you trap it by "giving" as it hits your stomach.

Watch out! An opponent is running toward you. Quick now! Do you dribble around her by kicking the ball ahead of you? If you do, your opponent is permitted to take the ball away with a soccer tackle. In soccer, to tackle is to take the ball away with the feet. The opponent tries to tackle the ball, not the person.

Do you have sufficient time for an instep kick to your wing man 30 yards downfield? How about a push pass to the teammate 10 yards to your left? Or a flick pass to the teammate coming behind you?

The defensive player is almost on you. You could lose the ball! Think fast!

There it is, at your feet. A quick dribble and you're past the opposing team member.

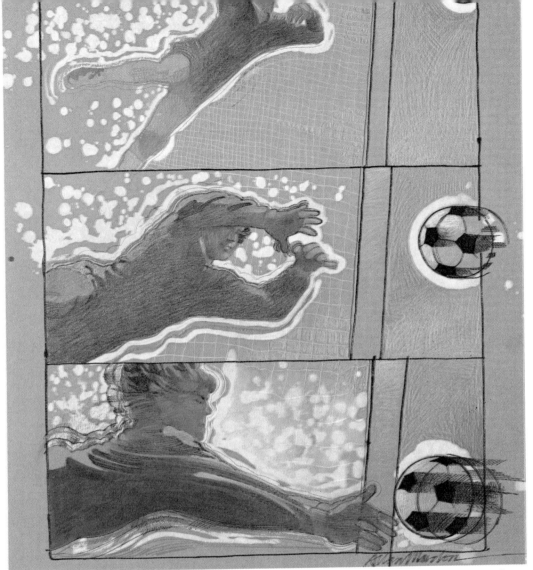

Line up the shot, and you kick a low line drive from 10 yards out. Score! Now you can see how exciting this game really is!

One of the reasons for the popularity of soccer is that you don't have to have a massive physique in order to play it well.

Speed is more significant than size in this game. Coach Simpson says that persons who want to develop sufficient speed should get into track.

But, the coach says, it's better if goalies are larger so that they can stop high shots.

They have to be quick, too, to get the low ones. "Lack of fear and good hands," he says, "are the most important qualities for goalies."

Coach Simpson also likes to maintain some bigger players for the middle of the field. "The ball is in the air more in the middle, and the big players usually are able to head it better than the smaller ones."

His best players are on the wings. "If the ball is coming right at a defensive player, it's very easy for the player to stop the play," the coach says.

"But if the ball is coming across the field from a wing, it's much harder for the defensive player to turn and stop it. We like to have a wing bring the ball down the side and then cross it in front of the goal. Then somebody has a chance for a good shot."

The coach uses various methods that give players a "feel" for the ball. One is a contest to see who can maintain the ball in the air for the longest period of time, using only the feet, the thighs, or the head.

It is preferable for a young player to learn to pass and dribble with either foot. Too many people learn to use only the right or the left foot. Then, in a game, they find that one foot is not sufficient, the Vermont coach says.

If you are thinking of becoming a successful soccer player, then continue to practice, practice, practice. It may not make perfect, but it will make better. It's preferable that the right methods be mastered when you first begin. Once you have mastered the game of soccer you will be ready to play an opposing team.

Hi-Me

Breaking the Ice

For a long time Jaime had wanted to come to the United States, but now that he was here, he wasn't enjoying it much at all. The main problem was the language.

Jaime was born in Argentina where the people spoke Spanish, and though Jaime had learned some English in school before he came to the United States, it just wasn't enough.

Oh, he could speak with the American boys, but Jaime often couldn't make sense out of what they said. One day Coach Gray introduced Jaime to the boys on the school football team.

"Come on, Jaime," Coach Gray said, "let's break the ice."

"Fine, but where is the ice?" Jaime answered, and of course, the other boys laughed, just as they had laughed when they heard his name. It was really pronounced almost the same as "Hi-Me." But whenever the boys met him, they would say, "Hi, you, Hi-Me."

Jaime knew they were only teasing, and though he tried not to let it bother him, it bothered him a lot.

Another thing that bothered him was football. It was a game Jaime knew nothing about because in Argentina they played soccer, not football.

Coach Gray wanted Jaime to join the practice games, but Jaime always forgot what he was doing and wound up playing soccer instead of football. He tried to learn the rules, but there were so many that Jaime became confused. He couldn't say some of the strange football words, and when he tried to say them, the boys usually laughed at him.

Jaime was so embarrassed that he stopped trying to play football, and he even stopped trying to learn the rules of the game. What did it matter, anyway?

So Jaime just sat and watched, wishing he was back in Argentina, where they played soccer and spoke a language he could understand!

Coach Gray kept asking Jaime to join the football practice, but Jaime said "No." He knew the other boys didn't want him because they only laughed at him. But he didn't say that to Coach Gray; Jaime was too proud to do that.

He was also too proud to tell his father what was wrong, but Mr. Valda, somehow, knew. He wanted his son to learn to enjoy the United States.

"I go talk to boys," his father said one evening, "and I ask them to teach you football."

"No!" Jaime shouted. "Once they heard you talk, they . . . ."

Jaime didn't finish his sentence.

"Maybe it is because I do not talk English so good?" Mr. Valda asked.

"Oh, no," Jaime said quickly, but inside he knew that was the reason. His father's English was even worse than his own, and if his father went to the boys, they would only laugh. They would laugh at both of them.

"I understand," Jaime's father said softly, "that my English is poor, but soon I learn more, Jaime. Until then, I will go watch boys play football, and maybe if I watch them, I can learn rules, and then I teach you."

"Remember, I was a good soccer player once," he said as he looked at Jaime.

Jaime felt tears in his eyes, and suddenly he was ashamed of himself because he had been ashamed of his father. And he was ashamed because his father had known how he felt.

"I would like you to watch the football," Jaime told his father. "We will go next Saturday and watch it together."

The next Saturday as Jaime and his father sat on the bench watching the other boys play football, Jimmy Ellis ran over to the bench to get a drink of water. "Hi, you, Hi-Me!" Jimmy called, and went back to the game.

Mr. Valda looked up at the funny way the boy said his son's name, but he said nothing. Then half time was called, and the players were resting on the field.

"Come, Jaime," his father said, "I have the soccer ball in the car. If you cannot play football, at least you can play soccer."

Jaime smiled because he was tired of sitting on the hard bench, and it would be fun to play a little soccer before the football game started again.

Taking the soccer ball out of the car, Jaime and his father walked down to the end of the football field where they began playing, kicking the ball, rolling and passing it to each other. Within a few minutes, Jaime was out of breath. He had forgotten what a good soccer player his father was.

He looked at his father and smiled, forgetting all about the other boys, football, and "Hi-Me." He forgot about Argentina and how he had wished he could be back there.

"Come, Jaime!" his father shouted. "Why do you stop so soon?" Jaime smiled as he ran to his father because he was very happy and very proud.

A Square Deal

Jaime was just about to ask his father for a rest from their soccer match when he noticed that the other boys had gathered nearby and were watching Jaime and Mr. Valda carefully.

Just then Coach Gray came walking over to see what was happening.

As soon as Jaime's father introduced himself, Coach Gray asked, "Aren't you the Carlo Valda who played on the world-champion team about ten years ago?"

Mr. Valda nodded and said, "I am he."

"I'm proud to meet you," Coach Gray continued. "I heard a lot about you when you played on the team from Argentina."

Jaime's father smiled and said, "Thank you."

"I've always liked soccer; in fact, I wanted to start a soccer team here, but I just don't know enough about how to play the game," Coach Gray said.

"It would be an honor to help you learn," said Mr. Valda to the coach, "and Jaime could help me."

Jimmy Ellis came up, examined the soccer ball, and said, "It looks like it would be too hard to remember not to touch the ball with your hands."

"It's simple," Jaime laughed.

"Simple!" Jimmy said. "Maybe for you, but not for me. Say, Hi-Me, do you think you could — "

Jimmy was interrupted by Coach Gray saying, "Hey, fellows, I want you to meet the man who's going to teach us to play soccer, Jaime's father."

The cheer that came from the boys made Jaime's heart happy.

"I do not speak English so good," Jaime's father told them, "so you must teach me as I teach soccer to you — yes?"

"Maybe you can teach us a little Spanish, too," Jimmy Ellis suggested with enthusiasm.

Mr. Valda nodded and said, "We trade Spanish and soccer for English and football."

"You want to learn football too?" Jimmy asked, sounding confused.

"My son wants to learn football very much," Mr. Valda told him.

Jimmy looked puzzled and said, "But Hi-Me stopped playing with us so we didn't think he was interested."

Jaime stood there silently, so surprised that he couldn't think of anything to say in response to Jimmy's statement.

"We'll teach you, Hi-Me," Jimmy said, still saying Jaime's name as if it was two words instead of one.

Mr. Valda put one hand on Jaime's shoulder, the other hand on Jimmy's shoulder, and said, "Then it's a deal square."

"You mean a square deal," Coach Gray corrected. They all laughed, and Mr. Valda was laughing about his confused English, right along with them. He didn't seem to be embarrassed, and suddenly smiling to himself, Jaime wasn't embarrassed either.

"By the way," Jimmy Ellis asked, "what's my name in Spanish?"

Jaime thought for a moment and he responded, "Jimmy is for James, and in Spanish, James is Jaime." Then he began laughing, as he said to Jimmy, "Hi, you, Hi-Me!"

Jimmy looked surprised, and then he laughed too, saying with enthusiasm, "Well, I hope this Hi-Me turns out to be as good a soccer player as you, Hi-Me."

He turned to Coach Gray and the other boys and shouted, "Come on, let's get to work!"

Think About This:

1. Why did Jaime want to go back to Argentina?
2. How did his father try to help him?
3. In the end, how did his father really help him?

Nancy Lopez

There was a time when the game of golf was enjoyed by only the wealthy, and very wealthy men at that. Few women played golf, but throughout the years, it became a game more people enjoyed.

Before long, there were professional golfers — people who play the game to win money. At first, these professionals were men only, but later, women became professional golfers, too.

One of the best-known women golfers of recent years is Nancy Lopez, who is of Mexican-American descent and comes from the state of New Mexico. When she was growing up, her father would allow her to go with him to the golf course to play.

It was very difficult for Nancy, who was small, to keep up with the grown-ups who were playing. She had to hit the little white golf ball more times than the others did to catch up with her dad, but she kept trying.

Nancy remembers, "One day Daddy was ahead of me, and he saw the ball roll past his feet. He told my mom, 'Maybe Nancy can really play.' "

Nancy definitely could play, and when she was nine years old, she won her first tournament. She kept on winning; she won the title of New Mexico Women's Amateur Champion when she was merely twelve. Everyone saw that Nancy was a great golfer.

Nancy won many more tournaments as she went on through school. She went to college and won the national championship title of all the college women golfers.

Then Nancy decided she wanted to play golf all the time, so she left to join the other women professionals who are called the Ladies' Professional Golf Association — or LPGA, for short.

It wasn't long before Nancy was winning again, but this time she was getting a lot of money for her golfing. Everyone began talking about this great young athlete. Nancy became famous and her picture was in many sports magazines.

In 1978, Nancy Lopez did something no other woman golfer had done before — she won five LPGA tournaments in a row. Only a few men in professional golf have done anything similar. At that time, she was excited to be called the best golfer.

Nancy isn't a big woman, but she's strong. She watches what she eats, gets lots of rest, and she definitely does practice all the time to stay as good as she is.

Professional golfers must travel to tournaments all over the country, and sometimes they even cross an ocean to play in other countries. It means living in hotels and flying in planes for almost an entire year.

Although Nancy usually travels alone, her dad and her sister often come to see her play, especially in the big tournaments.

It isn't always fun to be a professional athlete, and it has been especially difficult for women in sports over the years. People didn't pay attention to them until recently, which was a mistake. But people are definitely changing the way they think about women in sports.

Years ago, when little Nancy followed her dad around the golf course, no one knew

how famous she would become. Now Nancy Lopez is one of the best-known athletes in the world, and she's still young for a professional champion.

Nancy smiles and says, "I believe I'm gifted. I have this talent, and I believe I can do anything."

If you believe in yourself like Nancy does, anything can be possible in your life, and Nancy Lopez has proved that for the world to see.

Mirror, Mirror

The Other Moon

Dinky was a little yellow cat who was really a grown-up cat that stopped growing halfway.

He was as furry as other cats, and his whiskers were very long. But he was still much smaller than all the others.

Being little had good points, such as being just right to sit in a lap. And when he was hunting grasshoppers in the garden, he could hide behind the big yellow flowers.

But there were bad points, too, and that's what this story is about.

In the evening when the sky turned to velvet and the crickets sang from their hiding places, Dinky would sit in the window and watch the moon slip into the sky.

"Tonight," he would say as he gave himself a special bath and got ready to join the other cats on the fence, "I will polish my fur and sit on the fence with the other cats and sing to the moon."

Things never worked out right, though, because Dinky would get up on the fence, followed by another cat, and another, until he would be crowded right off the end.

That's how it went until the moon had turned to a silver sliver three times, and Dinky, who was very discouraged, finally gave up sitting on the fence.

One night he took a walk and was about to pass by the pond at the end of the road, when he saw something bright in the water. He went carefully to the edge of the water for a closer look, and what he saw made him purr in surprise.

There, as round as a plate, was another moon, only closer than the one in the sky. Dinky was so excited to find a moon of his own to sing to that he forgot to feel lonely. He began to make up a song to the music of the frogs in the reeds.

"O moon," sang Dinky. The watery voices of the frogs were quiet. "O beautiful moon, so shiny and bright . . ."

"Tonight," sang the frogs.

"O liquidy moon, like milk in a cup!"

"Drink it up!" sang the frogs.

Suddenly Dinky stopped his song, sighed, and told the frogs, "It isn't the same."

"I really want to sing on the fence with the other cats, but I'm too small."

"Not at all," they said.

"No one even sees me."

"Look and see," said the frogs, "look and see!"

Dinky looked over the edge of the pond and discovered something in the water — another cat; a very *big* cat!

Dinky looked again and found that the cat he saw was yellow and furry and had extra long whiskers. The cat in the water was Dinky.

"How can that be?" he wondered. "I know it's only me."

"I must have grown," Dinky said as he saw himself move on the water, "because I'm the biggest cat of all! I'm definitely big enough to sing with the others on the fence!"

So when Dinky went back to join the singing cats, he slipped up the fence like his own shadow, edged between two tough-eyed cats, and said almost bravely, "I came to sing with all of you, and I don't want to be pushed off the fence anymore."

"O.K.," said the tough-eyed cats, "so sing."

Dinky sang and sang and no one pushed him at all. But when he saw that the other cats were as tall as ever, and he was just as short, he knew he had only grown when he looked at himself in the water.

Dinky was afraid the other cats would see and push him off again, so he sat up straight and sang bravely, "O moon." Then he looked at the other cats and sighed, "O dear, O dear!"

"No fear," said a voice like the frogs' that seemed to come from the moon. "You're as tall as you feel, so no fear!"

Dinky opened his eyes and looked around and found that it was true. No one pushed him because now he felt big enough; they had made room for him and he was singing with the other cats.

"It doesn't matter," Dinky said. "If you think you're tall, then it doesn't matter how small you are!"

"If you think you are," said the voice.

"O beautiful moon!" Dinky sang, and it seemed to him that the moon nodded to his song.

Beverly Sills

Sometimes it is difficult to know just who we are in this world. There are so many things we do—go to school, play games, read stories, listen to music, help with work at home—and some of these things give us more satisfaction than others.

We are always us—you will always be you. But sometimes, when we do one particular thing, we feel more like ourselves than at any other time. For some of us it may be playing basketball or standing on our heads or painting a picture.

There is a very famous singer named Beverly Sills who feels most like herself when she sings opera. She is now known all over the world as a great opera singer, but Beverly Sills was once Belle Silverman, a little girl from Brooklyn who was not much different from many other girls.

Belle was the name her mom and dad gave her when she was born.

She also had another name then—Bubbles—but since Bubbles doesn't sound like a name for a great opera star, it was changed to Beverly.

Does that mean Beverly Sills knew she was going to be an opera singer? No, but she did know she enjoyed singing.

After she learned to sing by listening to and copying her mother's opera records, she went on to win talent contests for her singing.

Beverly sang on a radio program (that was before television), and people all over the country heard her voice. Beverly's mother knew that her daughter would have to have singing lessons if Beverly was going to sing opera.

Beverly and her mother would make long trips every week so that she could have good instruction. As Beverly grew, she knew she wanted more than anything to sing opera.

But opera is a very difficult art to learn since operas are generally sung in languages other than English—French, Italian, and German—because the people who wrote them spoke those languages. Besides that, opera is a difficult way of singing; the voice must be strong so that people can hear the songs in large theaters.

Opera music is not simple, and there are many notes of all kinds in just one song, or aria. On top of that, opera singers must be good actors.

All operas tell stories; they are plays that are sung. And many people are needed to sing all the parts, which is not an easy thing to do. But even so, Beverly Sills knew she was to be an opera singer. More than at any other time, Beverly Sills felt like Beverly Sills when she was performing in an opera.

Some people may say, "Oh, opera! Yuck! Who likes that? Who can understand it? Besides, you can't have fun with opera."

Well, that's just not true. Beverly Sills is still Bubbles in a lot of ways. She likes to have fun, tell jokes, and laugh, and she can make fun of some of the silly things that happen in operas and even make jokes about herself.

Beverly has gone through hard work and much traveling to become who she is. Singing one opera after another, one here and another there, she has still kept the delight and wonder that she possessed as a little girl.

After years of singing in operas all over the world, Beverly Sills became a big star in opera—or, as they say, a *prima donna*. She had reached the top of her world.

She sang for President Nixon, President Ford, and President Carter at the White House.

Beverly is also a wife and mother. She has written a book about her life, and she has had her own television show. She has decided to stop singing in opera in 1980.

She wants to direct operas — choose operas, singers, sets, and costumes and put all of it together. Only a few women do this today, but that is changing. Not many years ago, this would not have occurred.

Beverly Sills knew that opera was something special for her, and it came to be true. Beverly Sills or Belle Silverman or Bubbles, she knew who she was and she knows where she's going. And that's a wonderful thing for anyone to know.

Think About This:

1. How did Beverly Sills discover that she liked opera?
2. How important was the help her mother gave her?
3. Can you think of ways in which it helps to know exactly what you want in life?

The Panther

by Ogden Nash

The panther is like a leopard,
Except it hasn't been peppered.
Should you behold a panther crouch,
Prepare to say Ouch.
Better yet, if called by a panther,
Don't anther.

Land of the Big Night

"I see it!" shouted Nunuk. "I see the sun!"

"The sun returns!" cried his mother. "At last the Big Night is over!"

For eight weeks there had been no sun — only a glowing in the sky to the south. But now the edge of the sun rose into view, moved quickly along the horizon, then dropped from view. Tomorrow, Nunuk knew, the sun would stay a bit longer.

"Now the Big Night will end!" Nunuk exclaimed. "Now the snow will melt. Why must everything take so long?"

"Do not be anxious, my son," his mother said. "Many weeks must pass before the sun will be strong enough to make summer. Let us return to our job. We must clean the seal before your father returns from hunting."

Later, as Nunuk lay snug in his fur sleeping bag, he listened to his father tell of the hunt. The seal came early to the opening in the ice. With one strong thrust Nunuk's father had speared the animal and pulled it out on the ice.

"Oh, Father," pleaded Nunuk. "Take me with you tomorrow!"

"Wait, my son," his father said. "Wait until you are older. Now are the days for you to stay and help your mother and to play with the other children. And you must go to school. Be a boy a little longer."

The next morning Nunuk heard the bell on the schoolhouse as he woke the dogs for their breakfast of frozen fish. Stars sparkled over the snow, making enough light outdoors, but lights shone from the schoolhouse windows.

Then Nunuk had an idea! He would not go to school that day but would go out to hunt. When he brought home a fine seal that he had speared, his parents would be proud of him.

Nunuk ran back inside. Yes, the other seal spear was there. He waited until there was no one to see. Then he ran down the beach and out onto the ice. He scrambled over the pressure ridge that ran along the shore. The ice on the other side lay broad and white in the soft light. There was no sound other than the whoosh-whoosh of his shoes as he hurried along. He looked for an opening in the ice to which a seal might come for air. Then, to his left, he saw some small puffs of steam. That would mean open water. A breathing hole!

Nunuk crept to the edge of the opening and stood quietly. The spearhead on the end of the wooden shaft was a good one. The thong that held it was strong. Now if only a seal would come! The seal would push its nose up through the opening, and Nunuk would strike hard. The spearhead would come free from the shaft, the seal harpooned.

Nunuk waited long. The wind began to stir, and Nunuk turned away from it. Suddenly something gurgled behind him. He spun around, only to see a frightened seal slide from view!

"He'll come back," Nunuk told himself, as he stood with the harpoon. "This time I'll be ready! I will bring a seal to the village."

The sky brightened, and the sun came into view. Softly it rose and rolled along the horizon. Wind blew sharply in Nunuk's face as he watched. Again he turned his back to the glowing sky.

The wind grew strong, and Nunuk thought of the schoolhouse. It was warm there, and bright. Maybe he should have gone to school today after all.

Something gurgled in the dark water. A seal was coming! Nunuk's heart was pounding under his fur parka. Suddenly the water broke. He thrust the spear with all his strength, but too late! The seal was gone.

Nunuk was cold and hungry. He wished he hadn't come. Trying not to cry, he put the spearhead back on the shaft and tied the thong of the harpoon. The sky grew dark, and some snow touched his face. A storm was coming!

Nunuk began to run. But which way should he go? The snow fell faster, and he couldn't see. He was lost in the storm. Stumbling, he fell down. The wind took Nunuk's breath away. The wind — the wind was trying to tell him something!

"I must be calm," thought Nunuk. "I must not run. I must think." There was something about the wind — then he knew what it was!

The wind had cut sharply into his face as he watched the sun on the horizon. The wind must have come from the south, and home lay to the south!

Nunuk scrambled to his feet. He turned into the south wind and walked toward the shore. He reached the pressure ridge. As he climbed it, he saw the lights of the schoolhouse, far away in the distance. He tried to run but kept stumbling on the ice. The wind was strong and cold.

Then he heard someone call, "Nunuk! Nunuk!"

He saw some lights glowing through the blowing snow. He ran toward them, into the arms of his father.

Much later Nunuk lay snug in his sleeping bag. He listened to the wind as it roared outside. His mother worked on a fur parka, and his father was repairing a spear.

It takes time for the snow to melt, so summer can come, thought Nunuk sleepily. And it takes time for a boy to become a man. But every day is good.

Think About This:

1. Why was Nunuk so excited to see the sun?
2. Why did Nunuk do something so dangerous?

What a Racquet!

"I felt that if I really wanted to reach my goals, I would have to learn to lose! I couldn't stand to lose, and it used to just kill me."

These are the words of a real champion, Billie Jean King, and tennis is her championship game.

Billie Jean was born in 1943 in Long Beach, California, where her father worked for the fire department. A mix of Seminole Indian, Irish, Scottish, and English, Billie Jean says that it's the Indian in her that gives her strength.

As a child, Billie Jean played shortstop for a girls' softball team. She did well at bat and in the field, and she could throw well, too. She did so well that she was often asked to play shortstop or third base at fire department picnics.

When she was a little older, Billie Jean tired of softball. Her father then suggested that she try tennis, but he thought she would grow tired of that sport, too. But after her first tournament, Billie Jean was hooked.

Billie Jean bought her first tennis racquet with money she earned doing chores around her home. She played every day during the summer and after school and often she dreamed of being a champion. For hours at a time she practiced hitting balls over the net, working to improve her serve and her strokes. She even walked three and a half miles to school to make her legs stronger.

At the age of eleven, Billie Jean played her first tennis match against Marilyn Hester, a woman nearly ten years older than herself. Billie Jean won the match, but she still needed practice.

A few years later, tennis star Alice Marble became Billie Jean's coach. With Ms. Marble's help, Billie Jean proceeded to win her first tennis title, the Southern California championship.

The next year, Billie Jean lost to Wimbledon champion Maria Bueno of Brazil. Though Ms. King lost the match, she won a new coach, Frank Brennan! Mr. Brennan took Billie Jean under his wing when he learned that she couldn't buy the best strings for her racquet. He has been her coach since that time.

In the next few years, Billie Jean was collecting title after title. A win at Wimbledon in 1962 put Billie Jean King in the sports spotlight when she defeated champion Margaret Smith of Australia. Reporters wrote stories about Billie Jean, and her name became known around the world. It was an important win in Billie Jean's career, but the best was yet to come.

In 1964 Billie Jean traveled to Australia to train for three months. She had to exercise every day and build her strength. Her coach helped her change a few strokes, and she played in several tournaments. When she came back to the United States, she was a far better player.

1966 was Billie Jean King's year. She won her first Wimbledon singles title, and she became number one in the United States and in the world. In 1967 she won her first United States crown.

Billie Jean King is more than a champion, for she has been coach and friend to many young people starting in sports. She donates much of her free time to children, helping them learn about the sport of tennis. She shows them how to hold a racquet and how to hit the ball accurately.

Billie Jean is a friendly person, too, and she enjoys talking to the many people who come to watch her play.

At one time, she thought she talked too much during a game and started noticing that she even talked to herself as she played. Then one time she tried not talking while she played, and she won the match. She then decided that talking doesn't win championships. Now she talks to her fans before and after a match, but during a match she concentrates on her game.

In 1971 Billie Jean became the first woman athlete in history to earn more than $100,000. In that same year, Billie Jean won her first U.S. Open championship.

Another first in sports took place in the early 1970s with a tennis match between Ms. King and Mr. Bobby Riggs. Mr. Riggs was sure that he could defeat Ms. King. The event was on television all around the world. No one thought that even the best woman tennis player could beat a man, but everyone was wrong. Billie Jean King won the match, which was played at the big Astrodome in Houston, Texas. More than 30,000 people attended the match, and more people saw the match on television. More people saw that

match than any other tennis match in history.

Billie Jean is a busy woman, but she still finds time for her hobbies. She likes to read, dance, and play the guitar, and she also speaks out for the rights of all human beings.

Billie Jean King is a winner. "You're only Number One a few moments of your life," she says. "You've got to be able to laugh, or you just aren't gonna make it."

Getting Even with Jimmie Ray

The enemy, Jimmie Ray, was approaching, so . . . I hid behind a huge tree, and listened as his footsteps got closer. I really didn't mean to trip him yesterday, but Jimmie Ray got mad anyway and grabbed me. It's tough being nine years old. Boy, I wished my big brother was there because he'd fix Jimmie Ray. Oh, no! . . . the enemy was approaching, and I didn't know what I was going to do.

"Hey, Dinky," the enemy said as he held his hand out, "let's be friends and forget it."

What was he talking about? There was no way I was going to forget what he did to me.

I shouted back at him as I ran for home, "Jimmie Ray, I won't forget anything!" I began pondering a plan for revenge.

When I got home, my friends came to play, but I told them I didn't want to play. Not even watching TV, I sat in my bedroom pondering how and when I would get that tough Jimmie Ray.

Mom thought I was acting funny, and she made me come down to eat dinner. We had liver, but Dad didn't want it, and he told Mom so. Mom was already in a bad mood, so they had an argument. Then we were all pretty subdued for a while.

At last Dad said, "I'm sorry; let's forget it."

Mom smiled, and that was that. I left the table and went back to my bedroom, but I was still pondering how to get revenge on Jimmie Ray. I could hear Mom and Dad laughing and talking as if nothing had happened.

The next day I was still in my bedroom when I looked out the window and saw that all my friends were outside playing. Curious, my big brother stuck his head into my room and said, "Hey, Dinky, come to the park with me. My football team is playing today."

I couldn't turn that deal down, so I grabbed my coat and scrambled after him. I liked to go to the football games and cheer for my brother's team.

Excited, I got something to snack on and sat down to watch the game. The winner would receive a huge, fancy trophy. My brother had a lot of trophies, but I wanted him to win another one.

The game was tough, but my brother's team was winning. Then the quarterback threw a pass to my brother. A guy from the other team was running to stop the pass, but the ball went over both their heads. My brother jumped into the air to grab it, but when he came down, his hand unintentionally hit the other boy's face. I don't understand why the other guy started fighting my brother, but my brother wasn't going to allow that. Then they were both fighting even though people tried to stop them. I was mad as I could be when my brother and the other guy were thrown out of the game.

What an awful thing to happen — my brother sitting on the bench for the rest of the game looking sad. I watched my brother's enemy as he went to get some water. Then he walked over to his team, and I watched him the entire time.

My brother's team did win the game, so my brother got a fancy trophy with his name printed on it. But when we started home, an odd thing happened. My brother's enemy approached and said, "Hey, I'm sorry; let's forget it."

My brother shook his hand and said, "Sure, why not?"

I told my brother I didn't understand — how could he be friends with the enemy just like that? My brother said that it was a super thing for me to learn.

"Dinky, that guy isn't my enemy just because he got mad in the football game. We've all got to learn to be good sports or we'd use too much time thinking and doing bad things."

"Oh," I said, but I still didn't understand.

My brother put his arm around my shoulder and said, "Well, Dinky, what would you rather do — go after that boy, or have an ice-cream sundae?"

"A sundae . . . now I know what you mean. Let's go!"

We had a super time, and now I think I know what my brother meant — just forgive and forget. I missed a lot of fun while I was worrying about Jimmie Ray. Being happy is all up to me.

Think About This:

1. Why did Dinky want to get even with Jimmie Ray?
2. How can trying to get even with someone get in your way?
3. What made Dinky change his mind?
4. Why do you think his decision was a right or wrong one?

Consider the Chameleon

The Mail-Order Pony

Jerry and Sandra and their parents moved into a huge apartment house in the city. It was a fine modern apartment house, and they had fun learning how to run the elevator.

"There's no one to play with, though," said Sandra. "There are only grown-ups in this apartment house. I came up in the elevator with Mr. 8-A, and he must be almost a hundred years old."

"They're all too old," agreed Jerry.

"Then there's that silly rule about tenants not having pets," grumbled Sandra. "I'm sure our dog and the kittens are happy in their new home, but you and I aren't happy here."

"Oh, well, let's look around," suggested Jerry. Their mother made sandwich lunches, and they got their bicycles from the basement. Riding down the street, they passed other apartment houses and the modern building that was now theirs. Finally, they went home and, sitting on the apartment steps, ate their lunches.

The next day when they rode their bicycles they came to the end of a street and saw on a post a sign that read:

PET ACRES
Boarding Kennels
for Dogs and Cats
Mr. and Mrs. Austin

"Why couldn't Duchess and the kittens live in these boarding kennels?" asked Sandra, and the two children got off their bicycles and looked through the gate.

"Our pets wouldn't like being shut up in pens and cages all the time," sighed Jerry.

"I'd like to see some of the boarders," added Sandra. "Do you think they're all in cages and pens?"

Just then a man came from the red barn with a shaggy brown pony, and he slipped its lead rope over a small post.

"Welcome. Won't you come in?" he asked, smiling at the children. Jerry and Sandra said, "Thank you," and ran to the pony, who seemed to like to be petted.

"Maybe you know how to take care of a pony," said Mr. Austin. "We've never had a pony before."

"What's his name?" asked Sandra.

"Nobody knows his name," answered Mr. Austin, "or where he came from, or where he's going."

"You mean he's *lost?*" exclaimed Jerry.

"Yes, he arrived on the train and his tag was gone. Maybe he ate it." The children laughed, and the pony rolled his eyes and looked embarrassed, as though he knew more about the tag than they did.

"A man from the railroad brought him to Pet Acres, because he couldn't think what else to do with him," added Mr. Austin.

"It's a shame the pony doesn't have a name," said Jerry as he petted the soft brown face.

"The man is trying to trace him through mail-order and locate the person who sent for him," said Mr. Austin.

"A mail-order pony!" exclaimed Sandra. "M-O-P. Mop."

"We'll call him Mop," agreed Mr. Austin, "but he's a very fancy Mop."

Jerry and Sandra went every day to see the boarders at Pet Acres, where people going on vacation left their dogs and cats. Many days the children went galloping around the lawn on Mop and they often gave him carrots to eat.

Meanwhile, they began to get to know the other tenants of the apartment house. Mrs. 2-B invited them in for cookies, and Miss 8-F brought them library books. When Mr. 8-A met Sandra in the elevator, he always removed his hat and said, "After you, my dear."

One day the children found him in their apartment having tea with their mother, who introduced him as Mr. Herbert.

"I'd like to invite you to attend my birthday party," he said, and the children tried not to laugh. Such an old gentleman couldn't possibly care about balloons or birthday cake!

"On my birthday," he explained, "I always give a party for the boys and girls at the Children's Hospital. Every year I take a surprise to the party, but this year I had trouble getting what I wanted. Now I'll have to delay my birthday party, because the surprise didn't arrive."

"What is it? We wouldn't tell, " spoke up Sandra, but Mr. Herbert shook his head.

"You'll find out when you attend my party," answered the old gentleman.

The next time they went to Pet Acres, Mr. Austin had a long face. "This pony is eating me out of house and home," he said in a gloomy tone. "I called the railroad expressman, and I put an advertisement in the newspaper. It's a real shame, but I just can't keep our little friend anymore."

"Poor little mail-order pony," sighed Sandra.

"If you'll give us a day," suggested Jerry, "maybe we can locate a home for him."

They couldn't delay any longer, because Mr. Herbert was waiting at the apartment to take them to the party in his car.

The birthday party on the hospital lawn was the biggest they had ever seen. There were more people, more games, and bigger balloons, and there was even a magician. It was such fun they almost forgot to worry about Mop.

When the party was almost over, Mr. Herbert was introduced, and as he stood up to speak, he looked embarrassed.

"I want to tell you about the surprise," said Mr. Herbert. "I use the mail-order catalog to buy things, so I looked in the catalog and found what I wanted. Then I sent the money, and I waited, but the surprise didn't arrive, so I asked the company to trace it. They sent a letter saying that they were sorry for the delay, that the surprise must have been lost, and they agreed to send another . . . surprise . . . and . . ."

He suddenly looked down the driveway and cried,
"Here it comes now!"

"It's Mop!" cried Sandra. "He isn't lost anymore."

They all watched while a shaggy brown pony came
trotting up the driveway. A man led it across the lawn.

"It's *not* Mop," said Jerry. "This pony has a white
spot on his head and one white sock."

"No," agreed Sandra, "Mop is the other pony, the
one that got lost."

"The other pony is at Pet Acres with Mr. Austin," they told Mr. Herbert.

"Oh, my goodness . . . two ponies," said Mr. Herbert. "That really is a surprise, even to me."

Riding home, Sandra and Jerry told Mr. Herbert about Mop and about their own pets.

"You're welcome to visit the Children's Hospital and see the ponies," suggested Mr. Herbert. "And I think you and your parents should live in a house with Duchess and the kittens. I own the apartment building, but I also own some nice modern houses, and I'll rent one to your father."

Sandra and Jerry were so happy they couldn't say a word!

A Song of Greatness

(A Chippewa Indian Song)

When I hear the old men
Telling of heroes,
Telling of great deeds
Of ancient days,
When I hear them telling,
Then I think within me
I too am one of these.
When I hear the people
Praising great ones,
Then I know that I too
Shall be esteemed,
I too when my time comes
Shall do mightily.

Transcribed by Mary Austin

How the Prairie Pioneers Built Their Houses ────────

Imagine yourself in a large green field with not a tree anywhere in sight. Sounds like it couldn't happen, doesn't it? But a hundred years ago, that's the way many people found the prairies of this country.

Because there were so few trees, there was no wood to build houses, and it cost too much to bring wood from far away. So these prairie pioneers built their homes from sod, which is dirt held together with grass.

In 1862 the United States opened land in the West for people to settle on. Any family who wanted to start a farm there could have the land for free. As soon as land was chosen, a well was dug for water and then, while living in a tent, the family built a house.

Big pieces of sod were cut and dug up and then stacked one on top of the other, like bricks, until the family decided that the walls were high enough. Each piece of sod was stacked with its grassy side facing down.

The roof was the only part of the sod house in which wood was used. However, sod was put on top of the wooden roof. This time the sod pieces were laid with their grassy sides facing up, which made the roof green when the rain fell. Some flowers even grew on the roof. Even so, the rain came through the roof.

Some people had glass windows in their sod houses. Other people had to put paper over the holes made for windows. Boards were nailed together to make a door.

The walls inside were painted white. Most floors were dirt.

There were bugs and mice in most sod houses. There was little wood for making fires.

Children had to read by candlelight.

Despite these hardships, there were some advantages to living in a sod house; it was cool in the summer and warm in the winter. The wind couldn't blow it over and the sturdy house couldn't catch on fire.

Because it was so hard to build a sod house, the prairie family took good care of it. Many people later stayed in their sod houses while their new houses were being made of wood.

Today sod houses are a rare sight, but a few of them are still standing, and some unique people still live in some of them.

The Little Old Sod Shanty on the Claim

I am looking rather seedy now while holding down my claim,
And my victuals are not always served the best,
And the mice play slyly 'round me as I lay me down to sleep
In my little old sod shanty on the claim.
Yet I rather like the novelty of living in this way,
Though my bill of fare is always rather tame,
And I'm happy as a clam, on this land of Uncle Sam,
In my little old sod shanty on the claim.

Chorus

The hinges are of leather and the windows have no glass,
While the roof, it lets the howling blizzard in,
And I hear the hungry coyote, as he sneaks up through the grass
'Round my little old sod shanty on the claim.

Thomas A. Edison

When he was young, some people thought Thomas Edison was an unusual boy. Maybe that was because he was always asking questions. He had great curiosity about things. If no one would answer his questions, he would experiment. Maybe he could find his own answers!

One day Al—as his family sometimes called him—noticed that a hen could hatch chicks by sitting on eggs. A few days later, Al was found sitting on a nest of eggs. He was attempting to hatch some baby chicks. Of course, his experiment failed!

But that didn't mean Edison

Al started school when he was seven years old. He had lost none of his curiosity. When his teacher became angry at him for asking so many questions, Al told his mother.

Al's mother took him out of school. He had gone only three months. He never went to school again.

was going to stop learning—or asking questions. His mother showed him that learning could be fun! She made a game of teaching him to read. Al had never enjoyed anything so much. Soon he was reading one book after another.

When he was nine years old, Al's mother gave him a chemistry book. Edison set up his own shop and began doing all the experiments that were in the book. He had to find out for himself whether the man who wrote the chemistry book was right.

When Edison was twelve years old, he got a job as a "news butcher" on a train. A news butcher sold newspapers, candy, sandwiches, and peanuts. Edison needed the job so he could earn money to buy chemicals and other supplies for his experiments.

In one car of the train Al set up a little shop. In his spare time he would work on his experiments. He even printed his own newspaper—the first to be published on a moving train.

But one day something awful happened to Al! Some of the jars in his shop on the train turned over. They burst into flames and set the train car on fire.

The train conductor boxed Al's ears—hard!

Later on, Edison began to lose his hearing. Some people thought that his hearing loss was caused from the blows the conductor gave him. However, Edison blamed his deafness on something that happened to him at a later time.

Al was trying to get onto a moving train. The conductor, trying to help him out, grabbed Edison's ears to pull him up onto the train.

"I felt something snap inside my head," Edison said years later. "My deafness started at that time and has gotten worse ever since." A doctor wanted to operate on Al's ears, but Edison said no.

"I don't mind being deaf," he said. "It's easier to think about my experiments and inventions if I can't hear all the noise around me."

After Thomas Edison lost his first train job, he went around the country, working when and where he could. During this time he invented a voting machine that could record everyone's vote. Edison tried to sell his machine. But no one wanted it. Edison made a promise to himself. "I'll never again invent something that no one wants," he said. Edison kept that promise he had made to himself. However, some states today use a voting machine much like the one Edison invented and no one wanted.

When Edison was twenty-two years old, he went to New York City. He had little money and no place to sleep. A very kind man let Edison sleep in his office. Al helped the man when he could.

One day a machine broke down. After other people tried to fix the machine and couldn't, Edison made it run again. The man was so happy with what Edison had done that he gave him a job at $300 a month.

Edison liked to repair old machines. He also worked on his own inventions and made new machines. The head man at one company, Mr. Lefferts, liked Al's new machines. One day he asked Al, "How much money would you take for your machines?"

"Well," thought Edison to himself, "I could ask for $5,000 and hope to get $3,000. What shall I say?" At last he said, "Well, Mr. Lefferts, how much would you like to pay for my machines?" Now it was Mr. Lefferts's turn to think. "How would $40,000 be, Mr. Edison?" he asked.

Al could hardly believe what he was hearing. At last he would have all the money he needed to work on his experiments and

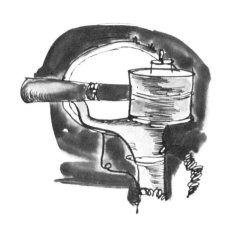

inventions! "Yes," he answered slowly, "I think that will be fine."

Thomas Edison was only twenty-three years old at this time. He used the money from Mr. Lefferts to set up a large shop. He hired many people to work for him, and he worked more than any of them. He improved the typewriter, and in 1876 he improved Alexander Graham Bell's invention, the telephone.

Before Edison worked on the telephone, people had to shout into it to be heard on the other end of the line. Edison made one that would carry voices a long way and into which people no longer had to shout.

One day, Edison got an idea. He made a paper figure of a man with a saw standing at the end of a funnel. When Edison shouted *Mary had a little lamb* into the funnel, the paper man began to saw wood. This was the beginning of one of Edison's greatest inventions, the phonograph.

Edison made a drawing of his machine and gave it to John, one of the men working for him. John was puzzled. He couldn't understand what the machine was meant to be. But in a day or two he had it ready, and he took it to Edison.

"This machine is going to talk," said Edison as he wrapped a piece of tin foil around one part of it. He called the men over to listen.

Edison got close to the machine and said, "Mary had a little lamb." When he stopped talking, the machine played back what Edison had said. The men couldn't believe their ears!

Edison worked on many other things. He made a light bulb and the first moving-picture machine that worked well. He received many awards for the things he made.

He kept on working to the end of his life. When he died in 1931 at the age of 84, he had invented over 1,100 things.

Born Is Better (Or Is It?)

It wasn't fair. Everyone else in her family was born, but she was adopted.

Her father was born, her mother was born, and her two older brothers were born. She had been born, too, but not to her mother. Oh, sometimes it made her feel so unhappy and lonely!

Anyway, her two brothers were allowed to do everything, and she didn't get to do anything at all.

They could stay up until nine o'clock every evening if they wanted to. Andy didn't like spaghetti, and he didn't have to eat it, so when the rest of them had spaghetti, Andy had a hamburger.

It wasn't fair.

And when Matt didn't like Mexican food, he had a hamburger.

But when *she* didn't want a hamburger (usually she did, but one day she didn't and said: "Mom, I don't want a hamburger today. I want spaghetti or Mexican food.") her mother just laughed and said, "Put some catsup on it to make it taste good."

Those kids that were born in the family had everything they wanted. Each boy had a bike with *two* wheels, but *her* bike had three wheels. *They* had boots they could *tie,* but *she* had to *pull* on her boots. *They* had a tree house, but *she* had a house made out of boxes in the dining room.

It wasn't fair.

One day she said, "Mom, do those boys get to do everything just because they were born?"

"Oh, no," her mother said, "it's just that they are older and so they are allowed to do more and get more choices than you."

"They can even go across the street by themselves," Rachel said.

"They're older," her mother said, "and they've learned that they should look for cars."

"I know that, too," Rachel said. "Sometimes I wish I had never been adopted."

"Rachel, we make rules for you to obey because we love you, not because you're adopted. We picked you, when we adopted you, but we could have had all kinds of other children — other boys and girls — but we picked you because you were just right for us, and we loved you the most."

"Then why can't I go to the drugstore?"

"Rachel, what do you mean?"

"The boys get to go to the drugstore and I can't, so I don't think being picked is so great."

Rachel's mother sighed. "Someday you'll understand," she said, and she hugged Rachel. "Now go and play because tonight we're going to the kennel to pick out a dog."

Rachel remembered and said, "Oh, yes, I almost forgot."

That night when Dad got home they all got into the car and drove to the kennel. Rachel had to sit in the front seat with her parents, but the boys got to sit in back and pinch and tickle each other and giggle and fight and get into trouble.

"Being picked stinks," Rachel told herself.

They drove up in front of the kennel, where Rachel could hear dogs barking and whining. When she heard the whimpers of small puppies, she pulled at her dad's hand and said, "Let's hurry; a dog wants me."

They walked up and down, looking in each cage. They saw big dogs with large barks; they saw medium-sized dogs with floppy ears; and they saw small dogs with lots of fuzzy hair and tails that curled.

Andy said, "I like that big white one with the huge paws."

Matt said, "I would rather have the one with the long ears and skinny tail."

Father said, "Who's going to buy food for a big dog like that?"

Mother said, "A small pup would be nice for our family."

Rachel walked around looking and looking until she saw a box containing tiny fuzzy puppies sitting on the floor. There was newspaper on the bottom of the box and a dish of water that had spilled on the paper and made the puppies damp and uncomfortable. The one that had a tiny white face and lots of short, thick fur looked at Rachel while Rachel looked back at the pup. The puppy's eyes were big, brown, and sad, and Rachel knew it was lonesome.

"Oh," Rachel said as she felt a lump come into her throat, "this one doesn't have anybody."

Andy laughed and said, "None of them has anybody."

"I know," said Rachel, "but this little puppy is so sad and lonesome. I can tell by looking at its eyes that it needs me."

When Matt leaned over to look at the whimpering little pup, he said, "I see what you mean. It has a special pleading look in its eyes sort of like the look you had when we went to adopt you, Rachel."

"Me? Did I have a special look in my eyes?"

"Yes," Mother said, "you had that look, too, and that's why we chose you."

"You could have had a lot of other little girls," Rachel said.

"Yes," her Mom responded, "just like we could have chosen lots of these other dogs."

"But you chose me," said Rachel.

"We sure did," said Andy, "and if you want that little pup, the one with the special look, the one that needs you, I guess it's O.K. with me."

Rachel gently picked up the little dog, held it close to her, and said, "Thank you."

On the way home Rachel sat in the front seat, close to her mother, cuddling the tiny dog in her arms. "I know how you feel," she said to the pup. "I was picked, too, but isn't it wonderful?"

Think About This:

1. What happened to make Rachel think that things at her house were not fair?
2. Do the same kind of things happen at your house?
3. Was Rachel's problem really because she was adopted? Why or why not?

Talking Leaves

How could the word of such a madman be trusted?

The Cherokee chiefs shook their heads and laughed at Sequoyah as he stood before them. They reminded each other that Sequoyah wasn't really one of them because he was only half Cherokee. His mother had been an Indian , and his father a white man. Even worse, Sequoyah had joined the white man's army when he was a young man.

The year was 1821 when Sequoyah stood before the most important Cherokee chiefs and told them that he could make "talking leaves." How could anyone make words come from leaves?

With Sequoyah was his daughter, Ah-Yoka, who was only twelve years old. Sequoyah had tried to make them believe that even she could make talking leaves, but how could this frightened child, who hid behind her father, make such big medicine?

No, the chiefs didn't believe Sequoyah could be trusted. By trying to make jokes with them, he was making bad medicine, so the chiefs became angry, and they frowned and murmured to each other.

Sequoyah tried to explain why talking leaves were important to the Cherokees. He told how he had first learned of talking leaves when he was in the army and saw the white soldiers look at pieces of paper with strange markings. These markings told them news of events that had taken place far away.

Sequoyah reminded the chiefs that the Cherokee people were now scattered across the country. If they were ever again to be united, they must be able to communicate.

Sequoyah told the chiefs that he had worked for twelve years and had turned the many sounds of the Cherokee language into only eighty written symbols. He believed that all Cherokee people could understand them and that, by writing the symbols on leaves of paper, they could communicate with others far away.

After talking with each other, the chiefs made their decision — they would prove once and for all that Sequoyah was a madman. They would put him to a test and, when he failed, he would be punished.

Sequoyah was frightened because if he failed the test, Ah-Yoka might be punished as well. It had seemed only right that she should be here with him, since she had been a great help in his work.

Sequoyah's wife had become angry because he had spent so much time writing on pieces of bark, so she had burned the bark and turned him out of his home. Ah-Yoka had stayed with her father even when angry Indians who feared his strange medicine burned their new home. And it had been Ah-Yoka who found a white man's spelling book in the woods. Because she understood her father's work well, she knew that the spelling book would be important to Sequoyah.

And it had been important. After studying the alphabet in the spelling book, Sequoyah made a set of symbols for the Cherokee language. Sequoyah's system was not an alphabet, however. Because the written symbols stood for different sounds, the system was called a syllabary. Since Sequoyah's young daughter had been able to learn all the symbols he was sure that Cherokee Indians everywhere could learn them.

Although he was frightened about the chiefs' decision, Sequoyah remembered how hard he had worked for this moment. He had come across the country to tell the chiefs about the syllabary. He thought about how the scattered Cherokee people might never again be a united people because they couldn't communicate with each other. He decided he must go through with the test.

It was not a difficult test. Sequoyah was told to wait outside the council house while, inside, the chiefs told Ah-Yoka some words to write down on paper. Sequoyah waited and worried until at last the door was opened, and he was told to come inside. As Sequoyah took the piece of paper, he looked at his daughter and was relieved to see that she no longer looked frightened.

Then he looked at the piece of paper and read aloud the words that were written on it. He could tell by the faces of the chiefs that he had made no mistake, that every word had been correct. The chiefs were delighted because they had spoken to a man who was too far away to hear their words. At last they knew what it was like to have a language that could be written as well as spoken. It took them only three days of studying to learn Sequoyah's syllabary.

Sequoyah was relieved to learn that he was to be rewarded instead of punished. He had not failed, and he was happy to have proven that he was not a madman.

Sequoyah was rewarded more, however, by seeing the Cherokee people communicate by using his syllabary. Within a few years it was being used across the country. Sequoyah's medicine was good for the Cherokee people.

Quicksand

Mark Hendrix finished his chores and lightheartedly went up to his room. He was changing into his baseball uniform when he heard his father's footsteps in the hall.

"What's up, Dad?" he called out, knowing that Mr. Hendrix never came back to the ranch house so early unless it was an emergency.

"That rain storm last night washed out the fence in one corner of our range," his father said grimly, "and the cattle are scattered all over the place. Son, I know you have a big game today, but with Shorty and Pete gone —"

Mark frowned and thought about the game, the biggest one of the season, and he was scheduled to pitch. Still, the look on his father's face left no question in his mind. "The game doesn't matter that much," Mark shrugged, trying to sound as if he meant it. "The ranch work is more important, so I'll get back into my work clothes right away —"

"There isn't time for that," Mr. Hendrix interrupted. "We'll have to leave now. It may take us days to round up the missing cattle, and we'll be lucky if we don't lose some of them in the quicksand near Boulder Creek."

Mark quickly saddled a horse, mounted it, and then followed his father to the far side of the range and through the washed-out fence. If they hurried — and were lucky — he might still get to the game in time to pitch the last few innings.

"Some of the cattle are over there!" Mark said, pointing off to the left. "How many are missing, Dad?"

"Twenty-three," Mr. Hendrix replied. "I drove the rest of the herd to the north side earlier."

Mark and his father circled out then, going in opposite directions to get beyond the small bunch of cattle. When the bunch was between them and the hole in the fence, Mark reined in his horse and waited.

"Now, Mark, close in now!" Mr. Hendrix yelled.

That was the sign Mark had waited for; he began to whoop and shout as he galloped straight for the startled animals. The cattle tried to get away from them — which was exactly what they were supposed to do, and because Mark and his father — plus the noise — were behind them, the cattle moved right through the broken place in the fence and back onto the Hendrix range.

"How many was that?" Mark asked as his dad galloped up alongside him.

"I counted fifteen," Mr. Hendrix said, "and if I had known it would be this easy, you could have gone to the game, Mark. But come on, let's get this fence mended and then find those eight strays."

Mark swallowed; it had been fun chasing the cattle back through the fence, and he had nearly forgotten about the game that would be starting about now.

"We'll split up and look," his father said when they were ready to continue the search. "You take the gully on the other side of the hill, and I'll head down toward the marsh by Boulder Creek."

Mark nodded and said, "Watch out for the quicksand, Dad."

"Don't you worry about me," Mr. Hendrix said, glancing at his watch. "We'll meet back here in twenty minutes."

Mark turned his horse toward the gully and galloped away, thinking about the game. There was still a possibility that he could make it if they found the strays soon. He rounded the crest of the hill and shouted, "Whoa!" Two steers with the double-H brand were eating grass directly below him.

Mark closed in slowly, and when he was within a few feet of the animals, he made a big loop with his lariat and tossed it over the horns of the nearest steer. Then he started back along the trail, slowly leading the roped steer; the other one followed close behind.

It took longer than he expected, but finally both steers were back inside the fence. Mark closed the fence to keep them from wandering out again and looked at his watch. It had been twenty minutes, but there was no sign of his father.

Mark waited a few more minutes, thinking about the game and wishing he were there; but he felt uneasy. At last he started along the trail to Boulder Creek.

Suddenly he stopped; several yards away from him, in the thick undergrowth on the other side of the creek, he saw the missing cattle. Surely his father would have seen them if he had come this way. He called, "Dad? Dad!"

"Over here, Mark!" a voice answered. "Over here!"

Mark knew his father's voice, even though it sounded hoarse and choked. His father's horse was tied to a shrub, but there was no sign of Mr. Hendrix. "Where are you, Dad? I can't see you."

"Over here behind the shrubs," Mr. Hendrix called, "but don't come too close — there's quicksand."

Mark slid off his horse, ran to look over the shrubs on the creek bank, and saw his father up to his waist in the quicksand beyond.

"Don't be frightened, son," Mr. Hendrix ordered, "and don't come any closer; stay there and you'll be O.K."

"What happened?" Mark called.

Even in this danger, Mr. Hendrix grinned as he explained, "This quicksand bed must be a small one. The cows were over on the other side, so I just thought it was safe all through here. I was going to drive them out of the shrubs on foot."

"I'll have to go for help!" Mark exclaimed, his throat dry.

"There isn't time," Mr. Hendrix told him, "I'm not going down fast, but you haven't time to make it to the house. Besides, there's no one there except your mother, and I don't want her frightened."

Mark stared at the liquid around his father and wanted to cry, but there wasn't time for that, either. "What shall I do, Dad? Tell me what to do!"

"Tie your rope to your saddle horn," Mr. Hendrix ordered, "and throw the other end to me; you'll have to pull me out."

Mark did as he was told and tied the rope; then he backed the horse as close to the bank as possible and, finally, he threw the free end of the rope to his father. It fell far short.

"The rope's too light!" Mark yelled. "I can't get to you this way so I'm going to wade into the creek with it."

"Stay there!" Mr. Hendrix commanded. "I don't know where the patch of quicksand starts."

Mark felt his heart racing as every minute his father sank a little deeper. He rubbed his sweaty hands on his uniform, thinking, "There has to be some way — uniform — of course!" Then he called excitedly, "Just a second, Dad!"

He looked hurriedly until he found a small, flat rock, just about the size of a baseball, quickly tied it to the end of the rope, and then went back to the bank. "Watch out, Dad!" Mark yelled, throwing the rock to his father.

It fell only a few inches short, and Mr. Hendrix grabbed the rope before the rock could carry it below the surface. "Perfect pitch, son," he called. "Now take it easy pulling me out."

Mark mounted his horse and moved slowly until the rope was tightened. Then even more slowly his father was pulled out of the quicksand.

When Mr. Hendrix was standing on solid ground again, Mark ran and threw his arms around his father. "Are you all right, Dad?" he choked.

"Thanks to you, Mark," Mr. Hendrix said, smiling. "Hey, you're getting your clean uniform all dirty."

"Who cares?" Mark asked. "Baseball doesn't seem very important right now."

"Oh, no? If it hadn't been for that great pitch of yours, I'd never have gotten out of that gooey stuff!"

Mark grinned and nodded. Sure, baseball was great; but even if he pitched a no-hitter now, it would never come close to the pitch he had made that morning.

"Come on, Dad," he said, "let's get these old cattle back where they belong!"

Think About This:

1. Why did Mark Hendrix decide that baseball was less important than helping his dad?
2. What knowledge did Mark use to save his dad?
3. Have you ever used knowledge gained outside work or school to help solve a problem?
4. If you have, can you draw any conclusions about learning?

Baseball's Lady Manager

If you think that the management of a professional baseball team is a job that only a man can handle . . . you're way off base!

In 1977 on Super Bowl Sunday, a woman named Patty Cox made the front page of newspaper sport sections all over the country. Patty was named general manager of the Oklahoma City 89ers on that day. She is the first woman ever named as general manager of a professional baseball team.

A man named Harry Valentine was the owner of the 89ers at the time. He named Patty Cox as general manager. He knew she could handle the job because she had actually been doing it for quite a while.

Usually baseball managers are men. Also they are usually old baseball players. Patty Cox knew that she might have a problem. Actually, she had very little experience with baseball. She had gone to a few of the old Oklahoma City Indians games with her father and had been the mother of a Little Leaguer.

Patty Cox is a good business woman, and the position of general manager requires that. She has managed to handle her position by going at it as a business rather than a sport.

Patty first became involved with the 89ers baseball team through her public relations job. Her ideas helped the people of Oklahoma City become interested in their home team.

When Harry Valentine put the 89ers up for sale, it was Patty Cox who talked a group of people in Oklahoma City into giving money to keep the team in town.

Being the general manager of a professional baseball team takes a lot of time, work, and talent from Patty.

On game day, Patty will provide help wherever it is needed. She has done many different things, such as selling tickets and running the scoreboard.

"It's a lot of hard work but I've enjoyed every minute of it!" she says. "If somebody's trying to do a good job and offers something that the people want, it will pay off!" Patty is sure that good baseball and her good management have paid off in fan support for her Oklahoma City 89ers.

Antonia Brico

Someone once said that to be a musician is to fly. Truly, it is a very special feeling to make music — any kind of music. There is something that sets us free. Nothing could be worse for a musician than to lose her instrument or have it taken away.

It would be like clipping the wings of a free bird. But such a thing happened to a musician named Antonia Brico.

When Antonia was ten years old and living in Oakland, California, she was taken to a concert of symphony music. She remembers, "When I went to the concert I thought, 'How wonderful! With a little magic wand you can make beautiful music.'"

The "magic wand" was the conductor's baton, the thin stick used to wave the orchestra together in time and melody.

Antonia began right away to study music. She began piano lessons and kept studying all through grade school and high school. She went on to the university and studied music there — rhythm, melody, history, and composing. Music had become Antonia Brico's life.

Antonia left America for Germany, where she went on with her music studies. One of her famous European teachers was Dr. Albert Schweitzer, with whom she studied the music of J.S. Bach. Although she played the piano well, Antonia wanted to play another instrument. She wanted to play the largest instrument of all — the symphony orchestra. Antonia wanted to become a conductor with the magic wand.

A good conductor of a symphony orchestra must know

all the instruments' parts. There are at least fourteen different musical instruments in a symphony orchestra, and sometimes more. And there are one hundred musicians playing these together. So, the conductor's part is very important and very hard.

The conductor keeps the orchestra playing along with rhythm and melody and feeling. The composer's musical ideas must come through the conductor. All the musicians in the orchestra must know their own parts, but the conductor must know the whole composition.

When Antonia decided to become a conductor, there were no other women doing this. Many people didn't think it was right to have a woman conductor. But happily for Antonia, not all the people in the music world had this silly idea.

For years, Antonia studied conducting in Germany. In 1930 she became the first American woman to conduct the famous Berlin Philharmonic Orchestra. Conductors praised her, along with composers and performers. She was only twenty-eight years old when all this happened, but already she was becoming famous.

Antonia returned to America and her home state of California. There Antonia conducted for the first time in America at the Hollywood Bowl. It seemed Antonia was on her way to a great career.

But then almost suddenly everything began to come apart. The people who did not like Antonia or any other woman conducting began their trouble.

A famous opera star said he would not sing if she was going to conduct. Even some women said it was wrong having a woman conductor. There were fewer and fewer orchestras asking Antonia to conduct them.

Someone told Antonia she had been born fifty years too soon. It seemed the music world was not ready for Antonia Brico. Her friends stuck by her and helped all they could, but it was too late.

Antonia just wouldn't be stopped. She organized an orchestra in New York, and all the musicians were women. Later Antonia decided to mix her orchestra equally with men and women. She said, "Women and men are together in life, so why not in the orchestra?"

Her orchestra, though, was not to last. Too few concerts were offered to them, and Antonia had to break up her orchestra. All the newspaper stories faded. "Girl Genius," they had called her, "The First Lady of Music." Now Antonia found she must make her living in another way.

She moved to Colorado and began giving piano lessons. From time to time she was guest conductor of orchestras in the United States, Mexico, Japan, and Europe. Years went by for Antonia and she grew older. Her dreams had faded too quickly. She conducted church choirs and an orchestra in Denver, but this was not enough. Mostly she taught young people who had come to love music as she had many years ago.

In 1973, one of her students from years before came to visit Antonia. Her name was Judy Collins and she had become a very famous singer and musician.

Judy thought it would be good to make a film about Antonia and tell her story. Antonia said yes and the film was made. The film was shown almost everywhere. The people who saw the film were moved in their feelings for Antonia. They saw a woman and an artist who worked hard, only to be pushed aside.

Now everyone who saw the film wanted to see and hear Antonia conduct. Orchestras all around the country began to call Antonia, asking her to conduct them in concert.

To Antonia, it seemed life was starting all over again. She was getting older, but now she felt young and strong. Antonia went flying here and there, conducting orchestras after many years of sitting in Denver.

But all those years when no one cared could never really be made up. Just like the free bird whose wings were clipped, Antonia could not fly in her music. And this hurt deeply for a very long time.

People these days are less foolish, in some ways, when it comes to women and music. It is the music, the art that is made, that is important. It makes no difference whether you are a man or woman — it's the song that's played that counts.

Antonia Brico, even as she grows older, still waves her magic wand and flies in her beautiful music.

On the next page is a copy of a program from one of Antonia Brico's concerts.

CONCERT 134
Dr. Antonia Brico, Conducting

8:15 p.m. OCTOBER 20, 1978

PHIPPS AUDITORIUM
Michaela Paetsch, Violin

Egmont Overture (1809) . . . . Ludwig van Beethoven (1770-1827)

Concerto in D Minor for Violin and Orchestra (1903) . . . . Jean Sibelius (1865-1957)
Soloist, Michaela Paetsch

INTERMISSION

Pavane pour une Infante Defunte (1908) . . . . Maurice Ravel (1875-1937)
In memory of Clyde and Bradley Kissinger
(No applause, please)

Laendliche Hochzeit (Rustic Wedding Symphony; 1876) . . . . Carl Goldmark (1830-1915)
I Wedding March   II Bridal Song   III Serenade   IV In the garden   V Dance

PROGRAM NOTES

EGMONT OVERTURE . . . . *Beethoven*

In 1809 Beethoven wrote incidental music for Goethe's historical play Egmont. His deafness had by then become fully established, causing him great emotional turmoil, yet only a year earlier he had completed the great Fifth and Sixth Symphonies. Political conditions in Europe were a shambles, forcing him on one occasion to move to his Vienna basement to avoid shelling by Napoleon's army; in the same year Beethoven was granted a substantial pension by Prince Lobkowitz and Archduke Rudolph. The overture has remained a part of the standard concert repertory ever since it was first published.

CONCERTO IN D MINOR FOR VIOLIN AND ORCHESTRA . . . . *Sibelius*

Sibelius was born in Finland in 1865. Although he was musically talented, he was sent to study law. At the same time he enrolled in the Musical Academy and soon relinquished law for music. He studied in Germany and Vienna, composing in the Germanic Romantic style. Returning to Finland, he was consumed with patriotism, wishing to have his country freed from the Russians. Thereafter his music was imbued with Finnish folklore and its people—and with the country itself. After his visit to the United States in 1914, he became recognized as an important international composer. He died in Finland in 1957.

Sibelius' only concerto was first performed in 1905 in Berlin, with Richard Strauss conducting. This intense but poetic work is in the Romantic style, with the solo violin and orchestra closely interwoven. It is one of the most eloquent works ever written for violin and orchestra.

PAVANE POUR UNE INFANTE DEFUNTE . . . . *Ravel*

Ravel was born in the Basque region of France in 1875. He entered the Paris Conservatory at age 14, and immediately became known for such remarkable compositions as Jeux d'Eau, Scheherazade overture, Pavane pour une Infante Defunte, and the String Quartet in F Major. After serving France in World War I, he retired to a villa and composed the music that placed him foremost in France and helped to usher in contemporary music. Ravel toured the United States and Canada in 1928 as pianist and conductor. An automobile accident in France caused brain injury, and Ravel died in Paris in 1937.

The Pavane was originally written in 1899 for piano, as were most of his works. His later orchestrations would give his piano compositions a new vitality. A Pavane is a slow, dignified dance, adopted throughout Europe in the 16th century.

Tonight's performance is dedicated to the memory of Clyde and Bradley Kissinger. In the recent hurricane in Baja California, Clyde and his 19-year-old son Bradley were tragically lost at sea. A promising young musician, Bradley had studied piano with Antonia Brico for 4 years. Mrs. Kissinger has performed in the last two of our operatic productions. The entire family have been enthusiastic supporters of the Brico Symphony. Our deepest sympathy goes out to the bereaved family.

LAENDLICHE HOCHZEIT (RUSTIC WEDDING SYMPHONY) .... *Goldmark*

Goldmark was born in Hungary in 1830. After studying at the Vienna Conservatory for 4 years, he taught piano, played violin in theater orchestras, and wrote music criticisms. Not until his Sakuntala overture was performed in 1865 did audiences and critics notice his music. Often his music is identified with Wagner and Meyerbeer, but much of it is Oriental, or exotic, in color and structure. Following the successful Rustic Wedding Symphony in 1876, he wrote a few minor works and died in Vienna in 1915.

Although Goldmark designated this composition a symphony, the Rustic Wedding Symphony is really a suite of five tonal pictures grouped around a Central European wedding ceremony. The musical style ranges from the sentimental to the joyful.

ABOUT THE SOLOIST—

Born in Colorado Springs 16 years ago to a family with a long and distinguished tradition in music, Michaela Paetsch began studying violin with her mother at the age of 3. She has won numerous competitions, including the North American String Competition sponsored by the Denver Symphony, the National String Competition in Chicago, and Young Artists' Competitions with the Jefferson Symphony, Colorado Springs Symphony, and Pueblo Symphony. In March 1978 Michaela was named concertmaster of the Colorado Philharmonic, after nationwide auditions, even though she was 2 years younger than the stated qualifying age. Michaela has performed with the Denver Symphony and in recent weeks with the Munich Philharmonic.

Our next concert, on December 8 at Phipps Auditorium, will feature the return of the distinguished Mexican concert pianist Maria Teresa Rodriguez, playing Brahms' Piano Concerto No. 2.

We are grateful to the Free Library of Philadelphia, Edwin A. Fleisher Music Collection, for the loan of the music for the Goldmark symphony.

ORCHESTRA PERSONNEL

FIRST VIOLINS
Jacqueline Maurer,
  Concertmistress
Pauline Dallenbach
Susan Day
Dorothy Dringman
Tom Fronapfel
Sun Hong
Arline Hunter
Barbara LeFleur
Mary McIlree
Barbara Peterson
Ottis Rechard
Lou Richards
Julie Seybold
Elizabeth Strom
Tom Stevanak
Alice Wood

SECOND VIOLINS
Jane Spence, Principal
Mabel Allen
Marian Barton
Beulah Berry
Nan Gaon
Phoebe Hansen
Lea Muth
Jeanne O'Dell
Marjorie Olsen
Ernestine Phillips
Beth Predhome
Maralyn Pusey
Diane Savage
Betty Schumann
Anna Schoettle

VIOLAS
Barbara Thiele, Principal
William Burkitt
Melinda Elswick
Eric Gutzait
Mary House
Alice McCuskey
Gloria Olsen
James O'Shea
Margaret Umbreit

CELLI
Beverly Woolery, Principal
Virginia Ainsworth
Nikki Barker
Jennifer Fouse
Robin Freedman
Jerry Isler
Virginia Lichty
John Peterson
Doris Rutland
Molly Singer

STRING BASS
Gilbert Johnson, Principal
Maynard Ayler
Lynn Fletcher
Judith Kerry
Sholom Pearlman
Helen Tinnin

FLUTES
Carol Phillips, Principal
Priscilla Patton

PICCOLO
Frankie Barnett

OBOES
Barbara Dutra-Silveira,
  Principal
Susan Berk

CLARINETS
Ronald Owens, Principal
Marjorie Ediger

BASSOONS
John Kline, Principal
Alice Henley

FRENCH HORNS
Gerry Baker, Principal
Thomas Baker
Sharon Bauer
Harry Heskett
Irene Stearns

TRUMPETS
Dallas Mathews, Principal
Lorelei Allison

TROMBONES
Douglas Harris, Principal
Frank Stretton
Larry Zola

TIMPANI
Zina Richardson

PERCUSSION
Kathy McCusker, Principal
Maureen Barton
Stephen Swanson

HARP
Marla Mathias

ASSISTANT CONDUCTORS
Lorelei Allison
Zina Richardson

LIBRARIAN
Roger Seick

PROGRAM NOTES
Dorothy Dringman
John Kline

DR. ANTONIA BRICO
Musical Director and Conductor

227

Look Behind You

The Odyssey

Introduction

The *Odyssey*[1] is one of the oldest stories in the world. No one is sure who wrote it. The writer may have been a man named Homer, who lived almost three thousand years ago. Homer lived in a Greek city alongside the Aegean[2] Sea, and he probably had his poetry put into writing. This was at a time when poets and storytellers went about the country telling their stories from memory. Although we know almost nothing about the man called Homer, his stories, the *Iliad*[3] and the *Odyssey*, have brought the history of the ancient Greeks alive to us today.

The *Iliad* is the story of the Trojan War in the country of Troy. The *Iliad* tells how the Greeks finally succeeded in capturing Troy. They rescued Helen, a king's wife, who had been kidnapped. This was done through the crafty plan of the king of Ithaca,[4] Odysseus.[5] When the war was over, all the Greeks but Odysseus and his crew returned to their homes. Odysseus and his crew wandered the seas for a long time. The *Odyssey* is the story of Odysseus's adventures and hardships on his way back to Ithaca.

In the days of Homer, the Greek people lived differently than we do today. They had their own ideas of

---

[1] *Odyssey* [ŏd′ ə•sē]
[2] Aegean [ĭ•jē′ ən]
[3] *Iliad* [ĭl′ ē•əd]
[4] Ithaca [ĭth′ ə•kə]
[5] Odysseus [ŏ•dĭs′ ē•əs]

gods and war and the roles of men and women. The Greeks believed that there were many gods and goddesses that had much to do with their lives. Whenever good or bad things happened, it was said that the gods were the cause. Although these gods and goddesses were not real people, they were both feared and respected by the Greeks. As you read the *Odyssey*, remember that the way the people think and act may not be the same as we think and act today.

There are many people who not only think the *Odyssey* is the first novel, but also the best novel of all time. But that is for the reader to decide.

The Search for Odysseus

The Trojan War had ended and all the Greek princes and warriors had long since returned to their homes across the sea. All but Odysseus, the king of Ithaca.

For ten years the Trojan War had raged and then ended, and then ten years more had passed. But still Odysseus had not returned to his wife, Penelope,[1] and to his son, Telemachus.[2]

---

[1]Penelope [pə•nĕl′ə•pē]
[2]Telemachus [tə•lĕm′ ə•kəs]

When Odysseus had left Ithaca, Telemachus was still a baby. Now he was a grown man of twenty years.

Telemachus longed to know the fate that had fallen to his father. A day came when he sat in his father's palace, sad with wondering. A stranger came to the gate of the palace. At first, no one paid any attention to him. Finally, Telemachus heard of the stranger and went to greet him. The hospitality of Ithaca was well known. And Telemachus thought that perhaps a stranger would come one day with news of his father.

When Telemachus saw the stranger, he put out his hand in welcome, saying, "Greetings, stranger. Welcome to the house of Odysseus."

The stranger, who looked like a young captain and carried in his hand a long bronze spear, took Telemachus's hand.

"Thank you, Telemachus. I am most happy to be here in the home of Odysseus, the famous warrior and king."

Telemachus led the stranger inside and made him comfortable in a part of the palace where they could be alone. Telemachus had water and a bowl brought so the stranger could wash his hands. Then food and drink were laid on a polished table by the stranger's side.

After the stranger had eaten, Telemachus told him of how his father had yet to return to Ithaca, ten years after the war had ended.

"He must have died on his way back," said Telemachus sadly. "Perhaps he lies beneath the dark waves of the sea. It would have been better had he fallen in the Trojan battle. A proper grave would have been made for him and his memory would last."

"Truly, you are the son of Odysseus," said the stranger. "I look at your face and eyes and I see those of Odysseus. I think, Telemachus, that your father has not died. Perhaps he will still return home through great danger and difficulty. Listen to me now and I shall tell you what you must do."

Telemachus's sadness changed to excitement as the stranger spoke these words.

"I would have you make ready for a voyage you must make to gain news of your father," the stranger said. "Sail first to the home of the old king, Nestor,[1] who sailed with your father to Troy, and ask what news he has of Odysseus. Then you must go on to Sparta[2] where Menelaus[3] and Helen live and ask them of your father's fate.

"If you should learn that your father is still alive, come back to Ithaca and continue to wait for another

---

[1]Nestor [nĕs′ tər]

[2]Sparta [spär′ tə]

[3]Menelaus [mĕn′ ə•lā′ əs]

year. You must care for Penelope, your mother, and keep your father's house safe and in good order. But if you learn Odysseus has died, come back and raise a proper memorial to him. Then you may seek your own fortune. You are a strong man of goodwill and will grow to be old and wise. But for me, I must now take my leave."

The stranger got up and Telemachus went with him out of the palace.

"I will not forget what you have told me," said Telemachus. "I believe you spoke to me from a wise heart, almost like a father."

The stranger said good-bye to Telemachus and walked away. But as Telemachus watched him leaving, something strange happened.

The stranger began to change form. He first began to appear as a woman, very tall, with a bronze spear in her hand. Then this form changed into a huge sea-eagle that stretched its great wings and flew up into the sky. Then Telemachus knew that the stranger was the goddess Athene,[1] who long ago had befriended his father.

When dawn came the next day, Telemachus got up from his bed and dressed. He put on his sharp sword and took up a long bronze spear. Two large hounds followed him from the house out to where the council

---

[1] Athene [ə•thē′ nē]

of Ithaca was being held. Telemachus had called the council together for the first time since Odysseus had left home. The wise old councillors had helped Odysseus rule the country.

One of them rose and spoke when Telemachus had been seated.

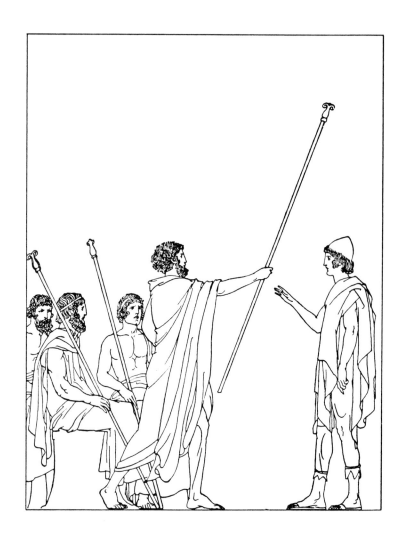

"Why have we been called together after so long a time, Telemachus? Is there news of Odysseus's return?"

"I will tell you why we have gathered," began Telemachus. "I have not received word of my father's return. At least not yet. I know we all share the same sorrow for Odysseus. But that is not the reason I have called you. There are some evil ones who would take my father's kingdom in his absence. Even now they are coming to the palace every day, eating up our food and wasting everything my family has built up over the years. They act as if they are our friends, but they have nothing but greed in their hearts. I am not able to drive these men away alone."

Another of the councillors spoke up.

"But what would you have us do, Telemachus? It is not our fault things are going this way. Your father has been gone twenty years. Perhaps someone else should now rule."

Telemachus could now see that some of the councillors had taken the side of those who would steal his father's house and kingdom. But not all the councillors felt this way. One of the oldest of them, named Mentor,[1] spoke up.

"What is this? Never have we had a king so gentle and wise as Odysseus," he said. "Now his son comes

[1]Mentor [mĕn'tər]

to us asking for our help, and you are not moved to give it to him. I say a time will come when these evil ones will be driven from this place. Why can't you rise up now and drive them out?"

But there was no one who took the side of Mentor and Telemachus. They just sat there and said nothing.

Telemachus spoke again.

"I have spoken to you in the council and you know the right and wrong of this. All I would ask now is that you give me a ship with a crew of twenty. I must sail to Pylos[1] and to Sparta to get news of my father's fate. If he should be alive and on his way back to Ithaca, I will remain here and wait another year for his return."

The councillors who had turned against Odysseus's family laughed.

"Well, well," said one of them. "Even if Odysseus should return, he is but one and we are many. Why should we care? If you want help, let old Mentor here get you a ship."

The councillors laughed because they knew there was very little Mentor could do alone. Then the council members left, leaving Telemachus alone.

Telemachus went for a walk along the seashore. Looking out across the sea, he cried, "Oh, Athene! You came yesterday and I listened and have tried to do

---

[1]Pylos [pī′ lŏs]

as you said. But these men have turned against my father and me. I have no ship and no crew to take me in search of news."

Then came an old man walking up the beach. He looked very much like old Mentor. But Telemachus could see by the shining gray eyes that it was none other than Athene.

"Telemachus," she said, "if you are to be a great warrior such as your father is, your voyage must come about. Go back to your house and gather food and water for your journey. While you are doing that, I shall gather a crew and get a ship ready. Then you must be on your way."

Telemachus went and did as Athene told him. While he did this, Athene, in the form of Telemachus, went here and there gathering the strongest young men in Ithaca for the crew. Then she went to a shipowner and asked him for his fastest ship, which he gave her.

Soon she returned to the palace looking like old Mentor and whispered to Telemachus, "Come. The ship is ready and you must leave right now."

Quickly, Telemachus went down to the ship and had his crew load the food and water aboard. Then, with a fair breeze that filled the sails, Telemachus set sail.

After some time, the ship came in sight of Pylos, the home of old King Nestor. Telemachus made his way to Nestor's palace, where he was greeted with great warmth. The old king gave Telemachus and his crew food and drink. After this, when they were alone, Telemachus spoke to Nestor.

"Nestor, respected king, we have come from Ithaca seeking news of my father, Odysseus, who long ago was by your side in the Trojan battles. I need to know whether he died there in Troy or is yet living. Tell me all you know, sparing nothing."

"Oh, my son," said the old king, "you bring sadness to my mind. Where are all those who were with me in that war against Troy? Gone, all of them. Now you ask me of Odysseus, who was closer to me than any of the others. There was no dearer friend to me than Odysseus.

"But tell me, how is it in Ithaca and with yourself?"

Telemachus then told the king of those who were trying to get his family's kingdom and of how only Mentor would help him drive them away.

"Ah," said Nestor with a knowing look, "who knows but that Odysseus will return and will himself drive these evil persons back to their own homes? You know Athene was always friendly toward your father, so she may be the one to bring about his safe return home."

"Nestor," said Telemachus, "you have been very kind to me, but you have told me nothing about what happened to my father, so I think now that he will never come home."

"Listen, Telemachus," said Nestor. "Go to Sparta and see Menelaus. He has come lately from a faraway country, and he may have heard news of Odysseus. Go to Sparta."

Telemachus spent the night in the palace of King Nestor and in the morning set forth with his crew for the country of Sparta. They soon came to this place, which was set among low rolling hills.

Telemachus made his way to the palace of Menelaus
and Helen. When Menelaus heard of the stranger's
arrival, he had him brought to the great hall to dine
with the king and queen.

Upon seeing Telemachus, Menelaus said to him, "I

can see from your looks that you are from a family of royalty. When you have finished your meal, we will talk of your home and your journey."

When Telemachus had eaten, Queen Helen said to Menelaus, "I think I can tell you who this stranger is, Menelaus. No one could look more like another than this young man looks like the great Odysseus. He could be no other than Telemachus, Odysseus's son left behind when his father came to rescue me from the Trojans."

"I have thought the same thing," said the king. "But why have you come here, Telemachus? Never has one come to my house that could be more welcome. For my sake, Odysseus went through many hardships. If he had returned to my country, I would have given him a city to rule over. But I know that Odysseus never came back to Ithaca."

At these words, Telemachus began to weep. Sadness filled the hearts of the king and queen as they thought of their lost friend.

Soon Menelaus began to speak. He told Telemachus of the adventure that brought the last news of Odysseus.

"After we had left Troy, my ship was blown to an island near the river that runs out of Egypt. We were running out of food and we could not get the weather to make our way back upon the sea. While there I met the daughter of the Ancient One of the Sea. He is called Proteus.[1] His daughter told me that Proteus could help us escape this island and that he could tell us of those Greeks who had become lost after the Trojan War. But she said that Proteus must first be captured.

"She said that as he came out of the sea, two of my men and I must grab him and hold him tightly. She said that he would change himself into many different shapes, but that we must not let go. When he had changed back into his first form, we could then turn him loose. Then we were to ask him our questions and he would have to speak the truth.

"And so we did this. The three of us sprang out from behind some rocks when Proteus came from the sea, and we held him tightly. First, he became a lion. But we did not let go. Then he became a snake, and then a leopard. This he followed with a wild boar, and then a flowing stream, and finally, he became a tree. All this time, we did not let him go. At last, Proteus returned to his true form.

"I asked him then what it was I must do to leave this island. Without a pause, he told me of the journey I had to make up the river to escape the island. Then I asked him what happened to the rest of the Greeks after they had left Troy.

---

[1]Proteus [prō′ tē•əs]

"Then, Telemachus, we learned of your father's fate. Odysseus, he said to us, was on an island far into strange waters. He was being held prisoner in a cave on this island by the goddess Calypso.[1] But Odysseus was not happy there and sat on the island weeping for his home. After Proteus told us this, he left us and returned to the sea.

"Now you know, Telemachus, that your father still lives, but he is being kept from returning to Ithaca."

Telemachus slept that night, knowing his father might still come back home. The next morning, he and his crew bid farewell to Menelaus and Helen, who gave Telemachus many fine gifts to carry back to Ithaca. As Telemachus sailed home, his heart was filled with hope for the first time in many years. Unknown to him as he sailed, Odysseus himself was on his way back home.

At this same time, Athene was speaking at the council of gods high up on Mount Olympus.[2] Athene spoke with such persuasion in the council that Zeus,[3] the father of the gods, was moved by her words. Zeus said the time had come for Odysseus to return to Ithaca. Zeus sent for Hermes,[4] the swift messenger of the gods. Zeus told him to go straight to Calypso's island and tell her the time had come to release Odysseus.

---

[1]Calypso [kə•lĭp′ sō]
[2]Olympus [ō•lĭm′ pəs]
[3]Zeus [zoos]
[4]Hermes [hûr′ mēz]

Calypso

Odysseus was a proud and brave Greek king. He had fought well against the Trojans in the great walled city in Troy. But that was years ago. Now Odysseus felt like a beaten man. So many hardships had already been conquered, but to what end? The brave Greek was no nearer his beautiful island home than when he started. And now he was alone. Of all his ship's crew, he was the last alive. And that once-proud ship whose gleaming prow had cut through countless ocean waves now lay in splintered pieces in the depths of the sea-god Poseidon's[1] kingdom.

Odysseus sat on the rocks by the beach on Calypso's island. He mourned the loss of his crew and his dream. Would he ever again see fair Ithaca, that most beautiful of island kingdoms? Would he ever again see his wife, Penelope? Oh, that he could once more see the smiling face of his son. After all these years, Telemachus must now be a strong young man.

[1]Poseidon [pə•sī′dən]   Poseidon's [pə•sī′dənz]

Odysseus feared that he would forever be held captive by Calypso. These sorrows and more passed through his troubled mind. He did not notice Hermes, the messenger of the gods, as he flew overhead on winged feet.

Hermes had been sent by Zeus, ruler of all gods. He flew to the island to ask that Calypso free Odysseus so he could return home.

The island was indeed beautiful. Near Calypso's cave was a group of fragrant trees — cypress, alders and aspen. Birds of all kinds made their nests here. Even sea-birds came in from the ocean. Around the mouth of the cave hung rich vines heavy with grapes. Four crystal-clear streams ran down the hillside into a meadow. Hermes stopped for a moment to take in the scene with all its beauty. Then he went into the cave.

Calypso sat before a fire of fragrant wood. She was singing in a merry voice as she wove at a loom with a golden shuttle. She looked up and recognized Hermes at once. Hermes could not see Odysseus anywhere. He did not know that Odysseus was down at his regular place on the beach, looking out across the sea with tears in his eyes.

Calypso invited the wing-footed Hermes into her cave and spoke.

"What brings you here, Hermes, with your golden staff? Come in. Tell me what is on your mind."

Hermes answered, "Zeus sent me. Why else would I come this far across the gray sea? The sea seemed to go on forever. And there was nothing along the way, no cities, no people, nothing. But when Zeus makes up his mind, I must go. He says you have someone held here who has been through much misfortune — more than anyone else who fought at Troy. All of his crew were lost, and he alone remains. Now Zeus says that you should send him on his way. He is not doomed to spend the rest of his days here, but should return to his homeland and rest in his own house."

Calypso listened to this with fear and a heavy heart. She did not want the brave Greek to leave her island. But then she spoke.

"It is all very cruel. I would like this mortal to stay here on the island with me, though he seems so sad. I rescued him from the dark sea when Zeus blasted his ship with a thunderbolt; I tended him and fed him the best food of my island. Now Zeus says he must return. Well, if Zeus insists, there is nothing I can do. But he cannot expect me to give Odysseus a ship, oars, and crew to carry him that far. Yet I will promise to give Odysseus directions that will bring him safe to Ithaca."

"Then do it," said Hermes. "You will avoid making Zeus angry. For he surely will be angry if you do not send Odysseus away."

With this, Hermes left the cavern and winged homeward as swiftly as he had come.

Calypso went to the beach at once to give Odysseus the message. When she found him, his eyes were red from weeping for his lost home. Though the beauties of the island were great, they brought nothing but sadness to Odysseus, who longed to see his own home once more.

Calypso said to him, "My unhappy friend, you need not stay here any longer. I am ready with all my heart to help you on your way. But you are going to have to do all the work. I will give you the tools to make a raft from the trees here, and I will stock your raft with bread and water so that you will not starve. Clothing, too, I will give, along with a favorable wind to carry you so you may reach your own country."

Odysseus did not believe Calypso. He answered, "You don't mean for me to leave here! Isn't this a trick to send me off on this great sea with nothing but a raft? I cannot trust your plan unless you give me your promise that you won't make new mischief against me."

Calypso smiled and said, "Odysseus, you are a villain to think such a thing about me. It only shows how tricky you are. I tell you I have no secret plans against you. I have some idea of what is fair. My heart is not made of iron."

So Calypso took Odysseus to the side of the island where great trees grew and gave him an axe. He cut down twenty trees. Then he smoothed them into lumber.

Calypso brought drills, pegs, and hammers the next day and Odysseus built a broad raft. He next made a mast and a rudder. Calypso wove cloth for sails. Then Odysseus skillfully fastened all of these onto the mast. Finally he moved the raft down to the sea.

On the fifth day, Calypso gave him new clothes, food, and water for the voyage. She reminded Odysseus to guide his course by the star they call the Bear. Then she said farewell to him. Odysseus felt a new surge of hope. He was finally on his way home.

It was not to be a safe voyage for Odysseus. The waves beat upon his raft. A great blast of wind snapped the mast into two parts. Odysseus was flung down on the deck with the waves breaking over him. The winds drove the raft to and fro. First the south wind tossed it to the north wind. Then the east wind caught it and sent it to the west.

In the sea was a nymph, Ino,[1] who saw Odysseus's troubles and pitied him. Ino had a magic veil. She decided to use it to help the poor seaman. Disguised as a sea gull, she rose from the waves with the veil held in her beak. She sat upon the raft and spoke to Odysseus.

---

[1] Ino [ī′ nō]

"Poor man! Poseidon, the god of the sea, is very angry with you. It looks as though the waves will surely kill you, but I will not let such a thing happen. You must do exactly as I say. Take this veil from me. Wrap it tightly around your chest. As long as it is upon you, you will not drown. When you reach land, take it off. Cast it back into the sea so it will return to me."

Still disguised as a sea gull, she gave him the veil and dived back into the sea.

Odysseus did as he was told. He took the veil and bound it around his chest. But he was still doubtful. He had seen many men lost in such violent seas, and so he would not leave the battered raft. As he worried about what to do, Poseidon, the sea-god, sent another monstrous wave, which shattered the raft. Odysseus had nothing left to do but cast himself into the water.

For two days and two nights, Odysseus was carried upon the waves, tossed this way and that. The magic veil did indeed keep him afloat, but the fierce winds and huge waves battered his exhausted body. On the third day the winds finally calmed and he caught sight of land. With his remaining strength, Odysseus began swimming toward shore. As he drew near, he saw waves crashing upon rocks all covered with foam. He was now terribly afraid. There was nothing before him but jagged rocks and reefs. To try and swim past those barriers meant certain death.

Just then, a great wave caught him and bore him toward the breaking surf. Odysseus would have been dashed to pieces against the reef if he had not grabbed one of the rocks as the waves beat about him. The backward drag of the waves pulled him from the rock and he went under. He struggled to break from the ocean's pull, for he knew that the current could hold him under.

With the help of Ino's magic veil, he finally surfaced, gasping for air. He began swimming along the shoreline away from the rough water. Before too long, he spied the mouth of a river where the water went into the sea. He began swimming toward it. There the waves did not break. The reefs had long been separated by the flowing waters. When Odysseus felt the stream's current pulling gently at him, his heart lightened. He began to feel safe.

"Oh, River," he cried, "have pity on me! Give me the help that I need!"

The river became quiet and he soon swam safely to the land. Odysseus was tired from his fight with the sea. His body ached and he fell upon the sand. As his breath returned to him, he remembered the veil and his promise to return it to Ino. He unwrapped the cloth and tossed it back into the river. The strong current snatched it up and carried it back away, back into Ino's hands.

But fear was still with Odysseus, and he said to himself, "What now? Here I am, alone, not knowing in what land I stand or what kind of people live here. What shall I do when night comes? I might freeze if I stay here by the river. But if I go into those woods, wild animals might eat me."

He chose the woods over the river and made his way until he came to two olive trees growing side by side. In their shelter Odysseus made a bed of leaves and fell into a deep sleep, resting from the terrors Poseidon had sent his way.

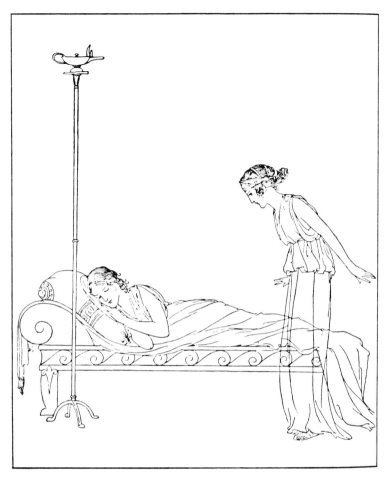

Nausicaa and the Phaeacian Games

While Odysseus slept, in the king's palace of this land called Phaeacia,[1] the princess Nausicaa[2] woke from a strange dream. In the dream, a woman came to her and told Nausicaa of her wedding day and how Nausicaa must make ready. The woman told her to take all the clothes from the palace down to the river for washing. She was to bring a wagon with mules to carry the load.

[1]Phaeacia [fē•ā′shə]
[2]Nausicaa [nô•sĭk′ ā•ə]

The woman in the dream was Athene, the goddess who was helping Odysseus to return home safely.

In the morning, Nausicaa did all that she was told in the dream. She called her servants to her and asked her father, the king, for the mules and the wagon. All the dirty garments from the palace were brought. Nausicaa's mother gave her a basket of food. Nausicaa herself drove the wagon through the fields and farms down to the river.

When they got there, the women unloaded the wagon and brought the clothes to a shallow part of the stream. There they laid the clothes in the stream and walked over them with their bare feet. After they had washed their laundry, they spread it out on the bank to dry in the sun.

With the washing done, Nausicaa and her servants bathed and played in the water before sitting down to eat the meal they had brought. After lunch, the clothes were not yet dry, so Nausicaa and her companions took a ball and threw it back and forth in a game of catch. They decided to play one last game and then return to the palace. When the princess threw the ball, it fell into the river. As it floated downstream, the women raised a cry that woke Odysseus, who was sleeping nearby.

Odysseus stumbled from his shelter. When he saw the women, he wanted to ask them for help. But when they saw him, they were frightened and tried to hide. Only Nausicaa stood still. She bravely faced him.

Odysseus stood away from her and spoke in a pitiful voice.

"I beg you, lady, to help me. I'm in bitter need. I would kneel to you now but I fear your anger. Have pity on me. I have been tossed upon the sea for twenty days in a raging wind before I came to rest in this land."

Nausicaa remained still. Odysseus was filled with reverence for her.

"I do not know whether you are a goddess or a mortal. If you are mortal, happy must be your father and mother and brothers. Never have I seen one so filled with beauty and nobility. Oh, lady, after all my many sore trials, to you, first of all, have I come. I know you will be kind to me. Show me the way to the town, but give me an old garment so that I may dispose of my ruined clothing. May the gods give you your wish and heart's desire."

Then Nausicaa spoke as a princess should. She saw Odysseus as the worthy man he was in spite of his wretched condition.

"Stranger, since you have come to our land, you shall not go without anything you may need. I will show you the way to the town."

Then he asked what country he was in.

"This is the land of the Phaeacians,[1] and Alcinous[2] is king. I am his daughter, Nausicaa."

She called her companions.

"Don't hide. This is no enemy, but a helpless man. We must befriend him."

They all came out and brought Odysseus to a sheltered place and gave him a garment. One woman brought some olive oil so that he might clean himself when he washed in the river. The oil was healing to Odysseus's skin, which was crusted and burned from the sea and sun.

When he had bathed and oiled and dressed himself, he returned to the princess and her companions.

He looked so much better that Nausicaa spoke.

"Look now on the man who just a moment ago seemed so terrifying. He is handsome and noble. Bring him something to eat and drink."

After Odysseus had eaten, Nausicaa came to him and said, "Stranger, if you want to go to the city, we shall be happy to guide you. But first you must listen to me. As we travel through the farms and fields, stay

---

[1]Phaeacians [fē·ā′shənz]
[2]Alcinous [ăl·sĭn′ō·əs]

close to the wagon and walk behind. But when we enter
the city, you must not be seen with us. If people see me
with a stranger such as yourself, they may speak un-
kindly. So I must ask you to go alone to my father's
house. Now listen and I will tell you how to do this.

"There is a grove, named in honor of Athene, in the city, and in the grove is a spring. Go there and rest by it. When you think we have arrived, get up and ask the way to the palace of the king. When you get there, go quickly to the great chamber. My father will be sitting there. Pass him by and go to my mother and ask for her help. If she will help you, you will have all the people of this land in your aid."

With that, they all started for the city — Nausicaa and her companions riding on the cart, and Odysseus walking closely behind. Upon entering the city, Odysseus did as he was told and came to rest in the grove of Athene. He waited there until he thought Nausicaa had come to her house. Then he got up and asked for directions. When he came to the palace he found that the great doors were made of gold and the doorposts were of silver. There was a garden of many fruit trees, apples, pears, and figs. Below that was a vineyard bursting with clusters of grapes. Odysseus stood there with many thoughts passing through his mind. Then with hope in his heart, he went in and made for the great chamber.

Now, that evening the captains and councillors of the Phaeacians sat talking with their king. Odysseus walked right past them and went straight to where Arete,[1] the

---

[1]Arete [a•rē'tē]

queen, sat. He knelt before her and asked for her help.

"Queen, after many perils I have come to you and your husband and your guests! May you all have a happy life. I have come to beg that you put me on my way to my home, for I have suffered long and I am far from my friends."

After having spoken, Odysseus went and sat in the ashes by the fireplace and bowed his head.

The queen then spoke.

"It is not right that a stranger should sit there in the ashes. Have him rise. Give him a chair and let him sit and eat."

King Alcinous took Odysseus's hand and raised him up and took him to the table, where he had supper brought to Odysseus.

"Tomorrow," said Alcinous, "we shall gather here for a great feast. Return and we shall speak of how we can help this stranger to his land."

The captains and councillors agreed and then departed, leaving Odysseus alone with the king and queen. Arete asked her servants to make a bed ready with warm blankets and purple sheets. Odysseus fell into it, and slept deeply into the night.

The next day, after the princes, captains, and councillors had gathered in the great hall, Alcinous spoke to them.

"After much wandering, this stranger has come to our land. He asks us for a ship and crew so that he may return across the sea to his home. Let us, as we have in the past, help him on his way. But before he departs, I want all of you to come to a feast in honor of this stranger. Bring the blind minstrel, Demodocus.[1] May his songs make us joyful."

So they went to the palace while the ship was being made ready for Odysseus's return home. All the princes, captains, and councillors gathered in the great hall. The feast began. Later, two men led in the blind minstrel, Demodocus, and took him to a silver chair and placed a lyre in his lap. When the feasting had ended, Demodocus began to strum his lyre and sing.

He sang of the Trojan war and of Achilles[2] and Odysseus, of their bravery and hardships. Hearing this, Odysseus began to weep, tears streaming down his cheeks. No one noticed his tearful face except the king. Alcinous wondered what could cause this stranger to weep so, but he said nothing.

When the song was finished, Alcinous spoke.

"Let us go now and begin some games and sports so that when he returns home, our friend, the stranger, may tell of the skill of our young athletes."

---

[1]Demodocus [də•mŏd′ ə•kəs]
[2]Achilles [ə•kĭl′ ēz]

And so they left the palace and went to the place where the games were to be played. All the young people gathered to try their skills and strength in honor of the king and queen and their guest. First, there was a footrace, followed by a boxing match, wrestling, and weight-throwing.

When the games were ending, the king's son, Laodamas,[1] said to his friends who had been competing with him, "Come, my friends, and let us ask this stranger whether he is skilled at any of these games or has any skill in sport."

So saying, Laodamas went up to Odysseus and spoke to him.

"Friend and stranger, you look very strong. Come along and try your skill at the games. You would enjoy it before your return to the sea."

"Laodamas," Odysseus began, "why bother me with games? Can't you and your friends see I am too sick at heart to be thinking of play? I have been through too much for too long. All I seek is my way back home. That is why I'm sitting here with your father and the court."

Then a brash youth who had won the wrestling matches, Euryalus,[2] came up and began to insult Odysseus.

---

[1]Laodamas [lā•ŏd′ō•məs]
[2]Euryalus [yə•rī′ə•ləs

"Oh, yes. I would never have mistaken you for an athlete. You appear to be some captain of a merchant crew who spends his life on some old ship, looking after his cargo and his profits. No! Anyone can see you are not skilled at sports."

With anger in his eyes, Odysseus turned and replied.

"You present a most handsome face to the world, but you have no brains. You have succeeded in making me angry. I want you to know that I am not new to the games. As a youth, I was one of the best, but much has been taken out of me since I left home. My days in battle and on the sea have aged me.

"But your words have hurt me. I will try my hand at the games."

Suddenly, Odysseus leaped to his feet and picked up the biggest disk of all. It was a huge weight, larger by far than those that had been thrown. With one swing he tossed it from his mighty hand. The stone flew lightly into the sky, well past the place where the Phaeacians had made their marks.

"Reach that, if you can, my young friends. And if you care, we can go on and have more — boxing, wrestling, or even running. I'm ready to meet any and all comers with the exception of Laodamas. I am his guest. I will not raise my hand to him. But any of the rest, come and try me now."

No one spoke. Then Alcinous said, "Well, well, stranger, you have shown your skill at the games. We Phaeacians may not be the best boxers or wrestlers, but let us show you something we do excel at — running and dancing. So, now, come, dancers!"

The dancers came to a place prepared. And Demodocus strummed his lyre and made music. Odysseus said to the king that he had never seen dancing so wonderful and graceful in all his wanderings.

The day came to a close and the king announced that gifts should be brought for Odysseus at the dinner that night in the palace. And all in the city came to honor the stranger.

Euryalus, who had been so insulting to Odysseus, came and brought a bronze sword to him as he spoke.

"Stranger, if anything I said offended you, may the great winds come and tear the words away. May you go safely home and be rid of all the sorrow you have carried."

Each of the twelve princes gave Odysseus a gift and King Alcinous gave him a gold cup. Arete, the queen, gave him a golden box filled with gold. Then, later, a warm bath was prepared for Odysseus, the first bath he had had since leaving Calypso's island.

After bathing and dressing in fine garments fit for the king he was, Odysseus returned to the great hall. He stopped on his way at the sight of Nausicaa.

"Farewell, stranger," she said. "When you are in your own country, sometimes think of me, Nausicaa, who helped you."

"Farewell, Nausicaa. I will never forget you. You will be remembered by all if I should reach my home, for you saved my life."

When Odysseus came into the great hall, Demodocus was singing. After he had finished, Odysseus spoke.

"You sing well of the Greeks and all they went through, almost as if you had been there at the walls of Troy. I would ask you to sing of the Wooden Horse that brought about the downfall of the city of Troy. If you can, I will be a witness to your greatness."

Then Demodocus sang. He sang of how one part of the Greeks sailed away in their ships. He sang of the others, led by Odysseus, who were hiding in the great Wooden Horse that had been taken into the city. And he sang of how the Wooden Horse stood with all the people gathering about it. The people had talked of what should be done with such a wonderful thing. He sang of how they decided to leave it as a gift to the gods and went to their homes, and he sang of Odysseus and his men, who then poured out of it in the night and took the city.

Hearing this song, Odysseus began to weep. This time the entire court saw him. The court began to ask, "Why does he weep?" No one had asked the stranger his name. Each wanted only to help someone in need. It did not matter who the stranger was.

Finally Alcinous spoke.

"Stranger, will you now be good enough to tell us what they call you in your homeland? Tell us where your home is. Tell us of your wanderings that brought you here. And tell us why you weep over the tale of the Greeks going forth to war with Troy."

Odysseus, who had wrapped his cloak over his head while weeping, unwound it and stood up. He turned to the entire company and began to tell them of his wanderings and adventures. He told of every tragedy that had befallen him and his crew.

The Cyclops

My name is Odysseus, son of Laertes,[1] and my country is called Ithaca, an island surrounded by many other islands. It is a very rough island, rocky and beaten by

[1]Laertes [lā·ûr′ tēz]

the sea. Ithaca takes its people and grows them strong and fearless. To me, there is no fairer land on earth, and it is there I long to return.

I will tell you now of my wanderings. My crew and I left Troy in our ship and were carried by the winds to the cape called Malea.[1] If we had been able to circle this cape, we would now be in our homeland. But a great north wind came and swept us away, driving our ship past Cythera.[2]

Nine days the wind beat at us terribly, carrying us away from all familiar lands. When the tenth day came, we found ourselves in a strange country. The people there were friendly. The land itself was enchanted. Strangers who came there forgot their past and cared nothing for their future. My men had left the ship while I stayed aboard. Now, they would not come back. They cared nothing for leaving this strange land. They wanted to dwell there forever.

I had to drag each of them back, one by one. I took them to the ships and tied them up with strong ropes. I ordered the sails to be set and we left that country as quickly as we could.

After a few days of sailing, we came to the land of the Cyclopes,[3] a race of fierce giants. Just off this land was a

---

[1] Malea [mə•lē′ə]
[2] Cythera [si•thir′ə]
[3] Cyclopes [sī•klō′pēz]

little island with a well of spring water. I ordered the ships to land there and we took down our sails.

At dawn the next day, we went exploring this island. We found wild goats among the hills and with our arrows, hunted them. After we had gathered nine goats for each ship, we looked across the bay to the land of the Cyclopes. We heard rumbling voices, the bleating of many sheep, and we saw smoke rising from great fires.

I called my crew together and said, "I think we should explore that other island. I will take my ship and part of the crew. The rest of you stay here and wait for our return. I want to meet the people who live here and see if they can help us on our voyage home."

So, we sailed across the bay and landed on the other island. Near the sea we could see a great cave. All around this cave were flocks of huge sheep the size of cattle. Taking twelve men with me, I left the ship and went onto the shore.

We went into the cave, which smelled of the sea and sheep. In there we found great baskets filled with cheeses and monstrous bowls of milk. My crew said we should take these baskets and bowls, along with some of the sheep, and return to the other island.

But I said, "No, this is not the way of things. It would be better to ask the people who owned these things to give of them freely, for we are strangers."

Although they pleaded with me, I would not be shaken. As it turned out, waiting for the owner was a mistake, for we were in for a very unpleasant surprise.

We had lit a fire, killed a sheep, and taken a few of the cheeses. After we had eaten, we sat down in the cave and waited for the owner's return.

At last the owner came, shepherding his flocks. The sight of him filled us with fear. As the red flames caught his face in its light, we could see the monster had only one eye in the middle of his forehead. In one arm he carried a huge bundle of wood like the trunks of many trees. With a great roar he threw these down in the cave. His voice was so terrible it rattled the cave like a tin plate. We were so frightened that we went further back into the darkness of the cave.

Then he drove his fat sheep into the cave. These were the ewes which he was going to milk. The rams and he-goats he left outdoors in a fenced yard. He then picked up a great stone, which he used to block the mouth of the cave. The stone was so large that not even twenty wagons could move it. That will give you an idea of how big he and the rock both were.

Next he sat down and began milking his ewes in an orderly way. Although he curdled some of the milk and put it away, he left the rest for his supper and for when he wanted a drink. After he had done all this, he made a fire and saw us.

"Strangers," his voice boomed, "who are you? Where do you come from? Are you traders? Or are you pirates who rove the seas and steal from other people?"

Though we were frightened, I was able to get my voice and answer him.

"We are on our way from Troy, driven off course by terrible winds across a great sea. We didn't plan to come here, but we lost our way. We are visiting you here today in the hope that you will help us. In the name of Zeus, who protects travelers from harm, I ask you for mercy and to receive us as guests."

The reply of the Cyclops[1] was chilling and pitiless.

"Stranger, how is it that you do not know of the strength of the Cyclopes? We do not fear or respect Zeus, for we are much stronger than he is. If I do not want you to live, even Zeus will not be able to change my mind."

His voice then became sly as he asked, "Tell me, where did you leave your ship? A place up the coast or close by? I should like to see it."

It was plain enough he was trying to get the better of me, and I met him with equal cunning.

"Oh, my ship," I said lightly. "It was wrecked very near your land by Poseidon, the god of the sea. The

---

[1]Cyclops [sī′klŏps]

wind carried our ship and hurtled it upon the rocks. We alone managed to escape with our lives."

With that, I pretended to be sad and tearful. But the brute made no reply. He jumped up and snatched two of my men. He took them and put them in a small cage made of wood. Their cries for help were useless. There was nothing we could do for them. We took ourselves to the back of the cave behind the sheep pen and there we lay down to sleep. We could hear the moaning of our two companions long into the night.

I awoke before dawn and crept up behind the pen to see what had become of my men. To my frightened surprise, the cage was empty and bones were scattered about the floor. The Cyclops was still sleeping.

My first thought was to draw my sharp sword from my side and slay the monster in his sleep. But after some thought, I realized that without the Cyclops, we would also perish. It would have been impossible for us to move the great stone from the mouth of the cave without the Cyclops's help.

At dawn the Cyclops got up and lit his fire and milked his ewes. When this was over, he once more snatched up two of my men. After he had eaten, he turned his sheep out of the cave, removing the rock as though it were nothing more than a mere curtain. But he replaced it as soon as he was outdoors. Then with a whistle that hurt our ears, he drove his flock off for their grazing.

I sat racking my brain for some plan that would free us from this dark cave and the giant Cyclops. And this is the plan I came up with.

Escape from the Cyclops

The Cyclops had a great staff made of green olivewood. To us it looked like the mast of some great ship that is used for long voyages. I went to work and with my sword, I cut off a piece of some ten feet. I handed it over to my crew to smooth down. When they had done so, I sharpened it to a point. Then I poked it into the fire to harden the point and hid it in the pen.

I asked for volunteers to help me lift the pole and push it into the Cyclops's eye while he was sleeping. Four of my best men volunteered, so we had a party of five.

At dusk the Cyclops came, herding his sheep. This time he herded every one of them into the cave, leaving none outside. Perhaps this was because he suspected something.

He went to work milking his sheep after setting the stone in its place. After he had completed his chores, he again took two of my men.

Holding my goblet carved of gold which I had brought from the ship, I went up to him. "Here, Cyclops," I said, "use this to wash down that meal. See what kind of treasures were stored in our ship. I saved this for you as an offering in the hope you would help us on our way. But instead, I find that your cruelty is more than I can bear."

The Cyclops took the goblet and drank from it. It gave him so much pleasure that he asked for more.

"Oh, be good enough to let me drink once more from your fine goblet," he rumbled. "And tell me your name so I may give you a gift you will value. We Cyclopes have goblets of our own, but none like this. Never have I seen anything so fine."

I handed him the goblet again. Three more times I filled it and gave it to him, and three times he drained it down. At last, when he was drowsy, I spoke to him with politeness.

"Cyclops, you wish to know my name. I'll tell it to you and in return I would like the gift you have promised me. My name is Nobody. That is the name given to me by my mother and father."

Then the Cyclops answered me with a cruel joke.

"Nobody, I will get rid of your crew first. You shall be last — that is your gift."

He barely got these words out before he collapsed, sound asleep on the floor. I went at once for our pole and thrust it deep into the ashes to make it hot. Then I spoke words of encouragement to my crew, hoping they would not prove to be cowards. When a fierce glow from the olive stake warned me it was about to catch fire, I took it out and brought it to where my crew was standing ready.

Seizing the pole, we drove it into the Cyclops's eye. With a dreadful shriek that echoed through the cave, he pulled out the stake. Then he began calling for the other Cyclopes to come to his aid. When these heard his shouts, they came running to the cave.

"What on earth is the matter, Polyphemus?[1] Why are you wrecking this quiet night with your cries and keeping us from sleep? Is someone driving off your sheep or are you being killed?" they yelled from the other side of the stone.

Polyphemus's voice rose out of the cave.

"Oh, my friends, Nobody has hurt me."

"Well, then," they answered, as though settling things, "if nobody is hurting you, you must be sick. Sickness can't be helped by us. You had better ask your father, Poseidon, for help."

And off they went, as I laughed to myself at the way a false name had tricked them. The Cyclops, roaring with pain, groped his way out and pulled the stone from the cave. But then he sat down in the doorway and stretched out both arms, hoping to catch us if we slipped out with the sheep.

I tried to think of a way out of the cave. Plan after plan, like fleeting birds, passed through my head. It was a matter of life or death and my men were looking to me. At last I felt I had a good plan!

---

[1]Polyphemus [pŏl′ ə•fē′ məs]

The Cyclops had in his flock some giant thick-fleeced rams with coats of black wool. Quietly, I tied the rams together in threes. Each member of the crew was tied under a middle ram. The rams on each side were to protect them. For myself I picked the ram that was the best in the flock. Grabbing him by the back, I curled up under him and held on to his thick fleece with a tight grip. Then, with fear in our hearts, we waited for the dawn.

When the East was spotted with red, the rams began to leave the cave and make for their pastures. The ewes stayed behind, bleating to be milked. Their master, though still in pain, ran his hands along the backs of his animals as they passed by him. But he never noticed my crew tied under his own wooly sheep. Finally, the big ram, with me trembling beneath him, stopped in the doorway. As he patted his back, the monster Polyphemus spoke.

"Oh, great ram, what does this mean? Why are you last to leave when you have always been first before? Today, you are last of all. Are you sad for your master's blindness at the hands of a wicked man who took my sight while I was asleep? Nobody was his name and I swear he is not safe yet. I would pound that Nobody who has caused this misery!"

So he let the ram pass out of the cave. When we had

put some distance between us and that terrible cave, I first freed myself and then untied my men. Then, quickly looking back over our shoulders, we drove the sheep down to the ship. My friends were excited when they caught sight of us. They began to cry for their lost friends, but I would have none of this. I told them to hurry and load the sheep onto our ship. Then we jumped aboard and pulled away with our stroking oars.

When I thought we were safe, I shouted to Polyphemus.

"Cyclops," I called, "you did not have the decency to be kind to your own guests. But your crimes have caught up with you, you who thought you were the stronger of us. Now Zeus has paid you back!"

This so angered the Cyclops that he threw a great rock which fell just ahead of our ships. When it hit the water, a backwash drove our ship almost onto the beach. Taking a long pole, I pushed the ship off while my crew pulled with their oars. When we were safely at a distance, the crew called out, "Don't you think you are silly to anger this monster? He almost wrecked the ship with that throw."

But I couldn't stop. In my anger I called to him once again, "Cyclops, if anyone asks you why you are blind now, tell him your eye was put out by Odysseus, son of Laertes, who lives in Ithaca."

The Cyclops let out a groan. "Alas!" he cried. "That was the prophesy! An old prophet named Telemus[1] once predicted that a man called Odysseus would rob me of my sight. But I always expected him to be a big person with great strength. And he has turned out to be a puny, good-for-nothing little runt. But come back, Odysseus. I would like to give you some friendly gifts and ask Poseidon to see you safely home. For I am his son, and he is the one who will heal me."

To this I yelled, "You do not fool me. Not even the great Poseidon will ever heal your eye!"

At this, the Cyclops lifted up his hands to the sky and called on Poseidon.

"Hear me, Poseidon. If I am yours indeed, grant that Odysseus may never reach his home in Ithaca. And if he does reach there, may he find all his friends gone and trouble in his home."

Then Polyphemus picked up a great rock, much bigger this time. He threw it with such force it missed our steering oar by inches. The wave carried us, though, to the farther shore, where the rest of our ships were waiting.

------

[1]Telemus [tē′ lə•məs]

We then sat down and shared the flocks and made a great dinner. After sleeping on the beach, we rose as the fingers of dawn nudged our eyes. I ordered everyone aboard and with everyone at their benches, we struck the gray waters with our oars. Thus, we left the island, and, with heavy hearts for the friends we left behind, we sailed on.

Circe

We sailed on until we came to the land where Aeolus,[1] the Lord of the Winds, who gives sailors good or bad winds, makes his home. Aeolus, with his six sons and six daughters, lives on a floating land that has a shining bronze wall built all around.

---

[1]Aeolus [ē'ə•ləs]

Here we were welcomed with sweet music and delicious food. For a whole month we stayed there, living with our kind host. I gave Aeolus news of the Trojan war and our trip home. As a favor he gave to me a big bag made of oxhide in which he had caught the energies of all the Winds. He tied the bag with a very tight rope of silver so that the Winds could not get away.

Then Aeolus called a wind from the west to blow my ships across the seas to Ithaca. But it was all to come to disaster because of the greed of some of the crew and my own weariness.

After nine days of sailing on Aeolus's fair wind, we caught sight of Ithaca and could see the signal lights on the shore. I thought the Cyclops's curse had been made for nothing and no more harm could come to us. So, as I was tired after tending the sails for all the time since we left Aeolus's island, I lay down in a deep sleep.

As I slept, the misfortune I had watched against took place. Some of my crew began to speak together.

"Here we have come back to our own land," they said, "but our hands are empty. But look at the gift Odysseus has from the Lord Aeolus. It must be a great treasure of gold and silver. Let us take just a little something from the bag for ourselves."

With more talk like this, the greedy took the day. They opened the bag, the Winds rushed out in a great howl, and soon the waters became a tempest, carrying the ships far out to sea. The crew fell to wailing and crying, and for a good reason: Ithaca was disappearing behind us.

When I woke up to this I had thoughts of throwing myself into the stormy sea to escape my grief. However, I soon came to myself and wearily covered my head with my cloak, lying down on the deck.

The winds brought us back to Aeolus's floating land. We landed and I made my way back to Aeolus's house, where I sat down. Soon he came out and spoke to me.

"What's this, Odysseus? Why have you returned so soon? Why are you not in your own country? Didn't I tie up all the winds that might blow against you?"

"Aeolus," I began, "it was my greedy companions that have done this thing. They opened the bag and let out the winds. I do not like to ask, but won't you help me once more?"

Aeolus then said to me, "I now see it is foolish to help someone whom the gods have turned against. Go away from my island. I will not help you. There is nothing I can do for you."

I could only walk away, back down to the beach and to my ship.

From Aeolus's island we sailed away with saddened

hearts. Next we came to the Aegean island where we were to meet Circe,[1] the Enchantress. For two whole days and nights we lay upon the beach, resting from the terrible times we had been through. On the third day I woke up at dawn, and taking my bronze sword and spear, set off to explore the island. Then I saw smoke rising up and went back to tell this to my men.

We drew lots to decide who should go to see if there were people to help us. Eurylochus[2] drew the lot and with a part of the company set forth, while I remained behind.

With twenty-two men, Eurylochus went out and found in a green forest glade a house built of polished stones. All round this house wild beasts roamed — wild wolves and lions. But as Eurylochus and the men came near, these beasts jumped upon them like friendly dogs, licking them with their rough tongues and cuddling against their legs.

But this scared the company and they stood wondering outside the gate. Then they heard the sound of a woman's voice singing sweetly. At this the crew shouted out and she who had been singing came out of the gate. She was most beautiful and walked with grace. When she appeared, she asked the crew to come inside. And in they all went.

---

[1] Circe [sûr′ sē]
[2] Eurylochus [yə•rīl′ ə•kəs]

But Eurylochus stayed behind and watched. He saw that she mixed something into the food and water she gave them. In an instant after they had eaten and drunk, she touched them lightly with a wand and suddenly they turned from men into swine; great bristling pigs.

Then she drove them out and shut them in a pigsty. She gave them acorns and corn to eat.

But for all this, being pigs, they still had the minds of men and they soon fell to weeping for their fate. Huge tears ran down their hairy snouts.

When Eurylochus saw all this, he quickly ran back through the woods and told me all. Taking up my bronze sword, I told Eurylochus to remain with the ship. I made my way back through the forest. I came to the house he had described and called out to the woman within.

When she came out she brought a cup of water into which she had put the potion that had turned the men into pigs.

When she handed me the cup I drew my bronze sword and pretended I was going to strike her. Circe shrank back and cried, "Who are you to guess my magic? You must be Odysseus, for I was warned of you some time ago. Put up your sword and let us be friends. I will treat you kindly and will give you no harm."

"No, Circe," I replied. "Not until you promise me that you will use no more trickery with me."

She promised she would not and I put away my sword. Then her servants made a bath for me and new clothes were set out to replace the rags I was wearing. Next came a feast on silver tables that were heavy with golden baskets of bread and meats and golden cups of honey-tasting nectar. But as I sat before this great table I didn't feel at all like eating.

When Circe saw me so she said, "What is the matter with you, Odysseus? Do you think I have put something in the food? I have sworn that I would not do such a thing and I keep my vow."

"Circe," I said, "how can I dine while my friends are swine in a pig-yard? If you want me to enjoy your feast you must return my crew to their true forms."

Upon hearing this, Circe went straight to the pig-yard. She touched each of the pigs with some oil. As she did this, the bristles and the snouts dropped away. My companions were once again themselves, but taller and stronger than they had been before.

After that, we all lived together on Circe's island in friendship. She did not try to trick us again. We lived there and feasted for a year.

But even for all this, we all felt a longing to return to our homeland. My crew came to me begging that I should ask Circe to help us on our way. She agreed and then told me of the many dangers we would meet on the voyage.

Circe took me by the hand and spoke.

"First you will come to the Sirens,[1] whose songs lure the sailors to crash upon rocks all around them. Their rocks are strewn with many bones of such men. But I will tell you how to pass by them with no harm.

"When you come near their island gather some beeswax and put some of it in the ears of your crew. But if you want to hear their song, have your crew tie you hand and foot to the great mast of your ship. And when you cry out for them to untie you they must bind you tighter. When you are safely past the place of the Sirens, your crew may untie you.

"Past the Sirens is another most dangerous place. On one side are great jagged rocks like the teeth of a bear. These rocks are called the Wandering Rocks. Not even the birds can fly safely here. Sailors who bring their ships too near are lost evermore.

"On the other way are twin peaks between which you must take your ships. One peak points to the sky. Its top is covered by great black clouds that never leave. No one can climb this rock, for it is as smooth as glass. But halfway up this misty crag is a cavern. No arrow from a strongest bow can reach the mouth of this cave. And it is past this rock you must sail.

"This cave is the home of Scylla,[2] a terrible creature. Her voice is no louder than that of a pup's, but she is a

[1]Sirens [sī'rənz]
[2]Scylla [sĭl'ə]

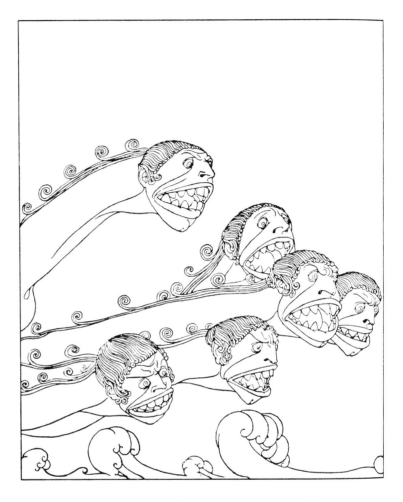

most hideous monster on whom no one would want to look. She has twelve legs waving in the air and six long necks, each ending in a horrible head. Each head has three rows of teeth in its mouth. Up to her middle she is sunk in the cave, but her long necks stick out of the darkness and down to the sea where she looks for any helpless creature.

"No crew has ever sailed their ship past Scylla without a terrible loss. From each passing ship she snatches six people from the decks.

"The other of the twin peaks is lower and the distance between them is less than a bowshot. Up on this crag grows a great fig tree, and under this, Charybdis[1] drinks the dark waters down. Three times a day, she spews the waters up, and three times, she swallows them down. May the gods keep you from the spot when she does this, for nothing can save you from harm.

"Now, Odysseus, you must sail close to Scylla's rock with all speed. It is far better you cry for the loss of six crew members than that of the whole ship."

"Yes, Circe," I answered, "but is there not a way I could stay away from Charybdis, yet fight with Scylla, should she come near my crew?"

But then she only called me a fool, always ready for a fight and looking for trouble.

"So, you are not prepared to give in to the way of things? I tell you, Scylla was not born to die. The monster will live evermore. She is a thing to pass up, a mean beast impossible to fight. Against her there is no defense; true bravery is in flight. If you waste time by her rock getting ready to fight, she will take twelve of

[1]Charybdis [kə•rĭb′dĭs]

your crew instead of six. Drive your ship with all your might past her rock, Odysseus!

"If you should get past these disasters," Circe went on, "you will come to the Island of Thrinacia,[1] where the Cattle of the Sun graze with immortal nymphs who watch them. These animals were not born in this world and they do not die of old age. If you can leave these animals alone, there is some chance you may return to Ithaca, though not without much hardship. Should you hurt these animals, I tell you that your ship and its men will be destroyed."

As Circe finished, the sun came up in the east. She left and returned to her palace, while my crew and I made ready to sail. Circe sent us a gentle wind that filled our sails and we were off into the gray waves.

---

[1]Thrinacia [thrə•nā′shə]

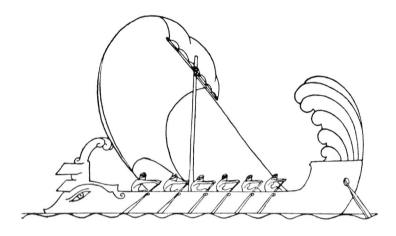

The Sirens, Scylla, and Charybdis

I gathered my crew about me and told them of Circe's warning. "Circe warned me of the Sirens and how we must not listen to their song and keep well away from their terrible place. The Sirens are beautiful, and their voices are such as you have never heard. To look upon them and follow their calling would mean certain death on the rocks. All who hear are doomed. But your ears will be filled with beeswax so you will be safe.

"I will listen to this song, but you must tie me tight to the mast and not untie me until we are gone from their voices. No matter how much I beg, move us swiftly past that terrible place or we will surely become like the white bones at the Sirens' feet."

Meanwhile we were coming close to the home of the Sirens and I called for a ball of beeswax. I pushed and pulled at the beeswax, making it soft under the warmth of the sun. I cut it into pieces and placed a ball of it in each man's ears. Then my men made me prisoner on my own ship. They tied me tightly to the mast. When this was done, they sat down to the benches and pulled with all their strength on the oars.

We were fast approaching the rocks and when the sight of our ship came to the Sirens, they broke into their beautiful song.

"Draw near, draw near, great Odysseus," they sang. "Bring your ship closer so you can better hear our song. No sailors have ever sailed their ship past this place without listening to the sweet song that we sing. None has listened that has not gone on a better man."

Their beautiful voices came to me from over the water and my heart filled with longing to go closer and listen. I made signs for my crew to turn me loose, but they just pulled harder at their oars. My mind was soon lost to the Sirens' magic. I had no thought but to join them. But two men jumped up and tightened the ropes that held me.

Soon we were past the Sirens. My crew pulled the beeswax from their ears and freed me from the mast.

No sooner had we left this place behind us than I saw a cloud of smoke ahead and the roar of a raging surf. My crew was so frightened that the oars dropped from their hands and fell into the sea with a splash. The ship stopped dead in the water. I went about the deck trying to calm the fear of my crew.

"My friends, we have met danger before. And I can't see that we face anything more terrible than when the Cyclops had us in his cave. But I found a way out of that and I'm sure that this day too will be a memory for us. I ask you to do just as I say. Pick up your oars. Return to your places and pull. We may have the luck to slide by and avoid all disaster."

"Give a wide path to that smoke and roaring surf you see. Stay close to the other side of the passage!" I shouted.

The crew jumped to my orders quickly. I could see no way to escape the trouble from Scylla, so I didn't speak of her to them. But I did forget Circe's warning not to do battle with Scylla, and armed myself. I went to the bow of the ship carrying a long spear. I wanted to spot Scylla before she saw us.

But no matter how hard I looked, I could not catch even a sign of her, though I looked over every part of the rocks until my eyes grew tired.

So we sailed up the passage between the rocks, groaning in terror between Scylla and Charybdis, who drank down the salt sea. When she spit up the waters, the spray filled the sky and the waters would bubble and boil as if on a fire. As she drank the waters down, the bottom of the sea itself roared and echoed among the rocks.

As our ship came near the passage, a strange quiet fell, like the moment before a storm. The crew stopped at their oars, looking up at the cliffs and down at the dark waters. I, too, suspected that all was not right with this quiet. The only sound came from the still waters that nudged at the sides of our ship.

I had the terrible feeling that all was not right. Without the oars, we drifted into the middle of the passage. I yelled orders to the crew. The sound of my voice, where no sound had been, woke them from their silent mood. Hands flew to their places on the oars and strong arms pulled with all their might.

Our move was almost too late. No sooner had I yelled than the sea returned to life. The waters began to bubble and boil with frightening noises such as we never before heard. Our ship had drifted right to the edge of where Charybdis lived under the water.

My men cried out in fear, but did not stop at their oars. This is all that saved us. As we struggled in terror with our ship, Charybdis started to drink down the waters. The seas began to move in a circle. As the water spun around, the center of the circle disappeared into the terrible mouth of Charybdis. Our ship was picked up by the current and spun around three times. Just in time, we were able to row clear of the danger.

My men were pale with fear and their eyes were fixed on Charybdis. Just then, Scylla flung her six necks down. Six of my most able sailors were snatched from our deck. Scylla had pulled them away before I could make a sound. The crew pulled on the oars as never before, all the while looking up at where our companions had disappeared. But Scylla showed her terrible faces no more. We were at last through the passage, but at a terrible cost!

We had escaped the Sirens, the many mouths of Scylla, and the terrors of Charybdis. We were now coming near Thrinacia, the home of the Cattle of the Sun. Though I wanted to land there, I remembered Circe's warning and ordered my crew to clear away from this place.

"Good crew, forget your troubles for a time and listen to me. I have been warned of this island. It is here that we would face the most dangers. We shall not land at this place."

My crew was heartbroken and one man, Eurylochus, spoke angrily against me.

"Odysseus," he said, "you are one of those hard men whose mind never grows tired and whose body is always ready. It is easy for you to speak this way, being made of iron as you must be. But is your heart made of iron as well? Your crew is tired and must rest from the sea. We need to eat a good supper and sleep on land this night."

The crew raised their voices and all agreed with Eurylochus.

"All right. I am one against many and you force me to go along. But I call on every one of you to make a promise that should we come across any cattle or sheep, you will not kill any of them to feed on. We shall sit together and eat the food Circe prepared for us."

The crew agreed and each one promised. Then we brought the ship round and landed on Thrinacia in a small sheltered bay. We set at once to gather fresh water and to eat our supper from the ship's stores. Then we took to our sleep.

When the dawn came we found we had no winds to take our ship from the island. The weather had turned against us.

So we stayed upon the island and the days went by into weeks and the weeks went by and still we remained. I gathered my crew about me and said, "My friends, we have food enough on our ship. Remember to keep your hands off the cattle and sheep, or we shall surely come to disaster."

As long as the bread lasted, my men kept to their word and kept their hands off the cattle. But soon the food on the ship gave out, and the men began to fish and hunt for food on the island. I went off into the woods to try to think of a plan to take us off this island. I looked to the gods, but all they did was send me into a deep sleep. And while I slept, Eurylochus was turning the rest of the crew against me.

"My poor friends," he began, "listen to me. All ways of death are terrible, but death by hunger is the worst. I say we should round up the cattle and sheep and make our food. Even if the Sun becomes angry with us, it is better to feel his anger than to die of hunger."

All the men were in favor of this awful plan and they set out to round up the cattle. They were already cooking the meat when I woke up from my deep sleep. As I started back to my ship, the sweet smell of the cooking hit me. I cried out, "Zeus, it was you that threw me into that deep sleep. And while I slept, the men were left to do this foolish thing!"

For six days the crew feasted on the Cattle of the Sun. On the next day the weather became clear and we went to the ship and made ready to set sail.

After we left that island, no other land appeared. Only sea and sky were to be seen. A dark cloud like a giant hand came and hung over our ship. Then, suddenly, an angry wind blew in from the west and hit us like a tornado. The storm snapped the mast like a dry stick. As the mast fell, it knocked one man far into the sea. Then Zeus thundered and great lightning bolts flashed through the dark sky and hit the ship. The whole ship groaned and the air was filled with the smell of the burning wood. My men were flung into the sea like so many dolls. They were tossed about like birds on the stormy waves. There was to be no going home for them.

With all this, I was flung from one part of the ship to another. Then a great wave tore the sides from her keel. I took a piece of leather and tied the keel to the mast. As I rode on these timbers, I became a game for the angry winds.

Soon the winds from the west went down. But they were quickly followed by a strong blow from the south. At this I felt a chilling all the way through to my bones. For I was returning to the rocks of Scylla and Charybdis.

All through the night I was carried along by the sea. In the morning I was coming near Scylla's rock and the dangerous waters of Charybdis. Charybdis was starting to drink the sea down. I was tossed right up into a fig tree. To it I held tight like a bat. I could find no place on the rocks to stand. And there was no way to climb further into the tree. So I hung there over those spinning waters and waited until Charybdis spit up my mast and keel. After a terrible wait, my hope came through.

My mast and keel popped up on the surface. I let go, fell down, climbed upon them once more, and began to row away with my hands. Thanks to the father of the gods, I did not catch another sight of Scylla, for I would truly have never lived through that terror again.

For nine days I drifted. Finally, on the tenth night, I was washed up on the island of Calypso. She treated me kindly and looked after me."

Odysseus finished his tale and all the king's court sat silent. King Alcinous spoke.

"Never would we Phaeacians keep you, Odysseus, from your home. Tomorrow we will give you a ship and a company to carry you to Ithaca."

All the princes and captains and councillors of the court were in wonder that they had met the great Odysseus. They each shook his hand before they departed for their homes. When the dawn shone forth, they all came down to the ship that was to take Odysseus home. There they gave him gifts.

At evening, just before the sun set, the king made a last feast for Odysseus. Then Odysseus went out of Alcinous's house and down to the ship. At once the sailors took to their oars and raised their sails. Odysseus lay down on the deck on fine cloth that had been spread for him. While the ship moved upon the waves as quickly as a bird can fly, he slept.

And as the ship lightly sailed on the waves, the man who had suffered greatly through war and the windblown sea, slept on. Asleep, he dreamed of things other than all he had passed through.

When the dawn came they were near the land of Ithaca. They landed near a cave and lifted out Odysseus, who was still sleeping. They laid him down on the fine cloth. Then they put all the gifts from the king and queen and the princes and captains and councillors next to him under an olive tree, away from the road. And there they left Odysseus. He would wake up in his homeland.

It was not long after Odysseus woke in Ithaca under the olive tree that Athene came to him.

"There is trouble in your home, Odysseus. There are men who have come to take your country and fortune away from you and your family. You must be careful until the time is right for you to strike. I am going to change your looks to that of an old man so that you will be recognized by no one."

Then Odysseus's skin went dry and wrinkled and his eyes faded to that of an ancient. His hair became gray and thin. And she changed his fine clothes to rags like those of a beggar and gave him a staff of wood. Then she left him. Disguised in this way, he walked into the city.

Odysseus went into the city and to the palace, acting like an old beggar. He was allowed inside, as were all poor strangers, and began to see that all was as Athene said. No one recognized him except his dog, Argos.[1] Even though the dog was very old and weak, when he saw Odysseus looking even as he did, Argos went up and began licking his master's hand.

Odysseus listened to the talk. He heard that the evil men were going to kill Telemachus and that there was no one but old Mentor to stand by his son's side. Odysseus knew he must act swiftly before any harm came to his son and to his city. He left the palace and found a place where he could be alone to plan.

That night Odysseus went to see Telemachus. At first Telemachus could not see that this was his father. But when he saw that Argos stood beside the old beggar, Argos, who let no man near him except Odysseus, he knew his father had returned. They held each other in a strong hug and cried tears of joy. Then Odysseus told Telemachus to go and get his weapons and bring them to him in secret.

---
[1]Argos [är′gəs]

Telemachus returned with his father's sword, spear, and a great bow no one could string but Odysseus. After they had prepared themselves, together they went to the great hall where the evil men were feasting. They threw open the door and the hall fell silent.

"It is over!" shouted Odysseus. "My troubles have ended and your time has come. I am Odysseus and I have come home." With that he put a bronze arrow in his bow. The evil men and councillors fell over each other as they tried to escape the hall and the angry Odysseus. Soon there was no one left in the room but the two of them.

Odysseus's wife, Penelope, then came in and saw Odysseus who now stood as himself, strong and noble. Penelope held tightly to her husband, whom she had not seen for twenty long years. The tears that rolled down her cheeks were tears of joy.

After many travels and much sorrow, Odysseus was home at last.

So ends the tale of Odysseus, who went to Troy with the Greeks. He had the plan of the Wooden Horse which brought the end to Troy. He faced the Cyclops, and escaped the magic of Circe. He heard the Sirens, and passed Charybdis and Scylla safely. He landed on the island of the Cattle of the Sun, and was held prisoner by Calypso.

And in spite of all these hardships and dangers, he was very lucky. He came back home to a wife, a son, and a peaceful home.

Glossary

Key to Pronunciation

Listed below are diacritical symbols and key words. The boldface letters in the key words represent the sounds indicated by the symbols.

/ā/	c**a**ke	/ē/	b**ea**n
/ă/	h**a**t	/ĕ/	p**e**t
/ä/	f**a**ther	/f/	**f**un
/är/	c**ar**	/g/	**g**o
/âr/	**car**e	/gz/	e**x**act
/b/	**b**oy	/h/	**h**ome
/ch/	**ch**ur**ch**	/(h)w/	**wh**ite
/d/	**d**uck	/ī/	p**ie**
/ĭ/	p**i**g	/p/	**p**et
/ir/	d**ear**	/r/	**r**un
/j/	**j**ump	/s/	**s**ee
/k/	**k**ite	/sh/	**sh**ip
/ks/	bo**x**	/t/	**t**op
/kw/	**qu**it	/th/	**th**in
/l/	**l**ook	/th/	**th**is
/m/	**m**an	/ŭ/	n**u**t
/n/	**n**ot	/ûr/	**fur**
/ng/	si**ng**	/v/	**v**ine
/ō/	r**o**pe	/w/	**w**ill
/ŏ/	t**o**p	/y/	**y**es
/ô/	s**aw**	/yoo/	**u**se
/oi/	**oi**l	/z/	**z**oo
/oo/	m**oo**n	/zh/	a**z**ure
/oo/	b**oo**k	/ə/	**a**bove
/ôr/	**for**k		**circ**u**s**
/ou/	**ou**t	/ər/	bitt**er**

A a

ac·com·plish [ə·kŏm′plĭsh] **ac·com·plished, ac·com·plish·ing** To finish: You can *accomplish* almost anything if you work hard.

a·dopt [ə·dŏpt′] **a·dopt·ed, a·dopt·ing** To take a child of other parents by law into one's family: After the child's parents died, another family wanted to *adopt* the child.

ad·van·tage [ăd·văn′tĭj] Any state or condition that helps someone: Brick houses have many *advantages*; for example, they are not painted.

Ah·yo·ka [ä′yō′kä] The name of Sequoyah's daughter (Native American, from the Cherokee language).

al·pha·bet [ăl′fə·bĕt] The set of symbols that spell single sounds of speech: English writing uses an *alphabet*.

an·cient [ān′shənt] Occurring in times long past: The wheel was invented in *ancient* days.

Ar·gen·ti·na [är′jən·tē′nə] A country in southern South America.

a·ri·a [ä′rē·ə *or* âr′ē·ə] A song, as in an opera, sung by one person to music: An *aria* is more difficult to sing than a simple song.

ar·ti·fact [är′tə·făkt] Anything made by the work of people: We knew more about the early Egyptians by looking at their tools and other *artifacts*.

as·sume [ə·sōōm′] **as·sumed, as·sum·ing** 1. To take as if true; suppose. 2. To take on a shape, role, or look: Runners *assume* a crouching position just before the gun.

B b

bi·cy·cle [bī′sĭk·əl] A vehicle with two large wheels, one behind the other: People ride *bicycles* by moving foot pedals.

board [bôrd] **board·ed, board·ing** 1. A flat, thin piece of wood. 2. To give or get food, especially for pay: The building is a *boarding* house, where people pay to eat and sleep.

Bri·co, An·ton·ia [brē′kō, än·tōn′yä] A famous woman orchestra conductor.

brim [brĭm] 1. The upper edge of a cup or bowl. 2. A rim that sticks out, as on a hat: A hat with a big *brim* keeps the sun out of my eyes.

bron·co *or* **bron·cho** [brŏng′kō] A small, wild horse of the western United States: The ranch hand fell off the bucking *bronco*.

bru·in [brōō′ĭn] A bear: A grizzly bear is a large *bruin*.

Bue·no, Ma·ri·a [bwĕ′nō, mä·rē′ä] A woman tennis champion from Brazil.

C c

ca·per [kā′pər] **ca·pered, ca·per·ing** To leap or skip playfully: We watched the children *caper* around the park.

cat·a·log [kăt′ə·lôg] A book that lists, and usually describes, names or objects: A sales *catalog* describes things a company sells.

com·mu·ni·cate [kə·myōō′nə·kāt] **com·mu·ni·cat·ed, com·mu·ni·cat·ing** To give or exchange thoughts, information, or messages: Writing allows people to *communicate*.

con·cen·trate [kŏn′sən·trāt] **con·cen·trat·ed, con·cen·trat·ing** To fix or gather one's whole attention: They *concentrate* on their reading and never hear anyone call.

con·cert [kŏn′sûrt] A musical program or performance: We enjoyed the piano *concert*.

con·struct [kən·strŭkt′] **con·struct·ed, con·struct·ing** To make by putting parts together; build: They are *constructing* the new house.

cun·ning [kŭn′ĭng] Slyness or trickery in getting something: Cats use *cunning* to catch mice.

D d

de·feat [dĭ·fēt′] **de·feat·ed, de·feat·ing** To win over; beat: The better player should *defeat* the poorer player.

de·lay [dĭ·lā′] **de·layed, de·lay·ing** To make late by stopping or slowing up: Rain will *delay* the baseball game.

dif·fi·cul·ty [dĭf′ə·kŭl′tē] Something that is not easy to do or understand: We saw ripe apples on high branches, but our *difficulties* lay in reaching them.

dock [dŏk] A platform built beside or out from a shore where ships or boats tie up: Please tie the boat to the *dock* so it will not drift away.

dow·ry [dou′rē] The money or property a bride brings to her husband when they marry: The young lady's *dowry* included a house and land.

dug·out [dŭg′out′] A low, covered shelter at a baseball diamond, in which players sit: The whole team sat in the *dugout* until the rain stopped.

E e

el·e·ment [ĕl′ə·mənt] Any of a number of substances of which all matter is made: Gold is an *element* found in rocks.

es·teem [ə·stēm′] **es·teemed, es·teem·ing** To respect; think something or someone has great worth: Because they were kind and honest, they were *esteemed*.

ewe [yōō] A female sheep: The lambs played near some *ewes*.

ex·press·man [ĭk·sprĕs′măn *or* ĭk·sprĕs′mən] A person working for a company that moves packages or money quickly from one place to another: The railroad *expressman* takes care of packages sent by train.

F f

fare [fâr] 1. The money charged to ride a bus or train. 2. Food and drink: Their usual lunch *fare* was a tuna sandwich and milk.

foul [foul] **fouled, foul·ing** 1. Very dirty, stinking, or rotten. 2. To bat the ball outside the boundary lines: Several batters *fouled* out during the game.

G g

gal·ler·y [găl′ər·ē]
A place where works of art are shown: The artist hoped many people would see the paintings in the *galleries*.

ghet·to [gĕt′ō] Any part of a city or town crowded with a minority group or the very poor: The word *ghetto* usually describes parts of large, American cities.

goal·ie [gō′lē]
A player who guards the team's goal: Their *goalie* kept the opposing team from scoring.

H h

Hai Lu [hī lōō] 1. A town in China. 2. A woman's name (Chinese).

har·mo·ny [här′mə·nē] A peaceful condition; agreement in feeling and ways of acting: Dogs and cats sometimes live together in *harmony*.

har·poon [här·pōōn′]
A pointed weapon with a rope attached: Large fish can be speared with a *harpoon*.

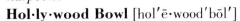

Hol·ly·wood Bowl [hol′ē·wood′bōl′]
A large outdoor theater in Hollywood, California, where many symphonies and concerts are performed.

I i

in·step [ĭn′stĕp′]
The curved upper part of the human foot, from the toes to the ankle: Shoes pinch my *instep*.

in·tro·duce [ĭn′trə·d(y)ōōs′] **in·tro·duced, in·tro·duc·ing** To make acquainted face to face; present: Have I *introduced* you to my sister?

K k

ken·nel [kĕn′əl]
A place where dogs and other animals are fed and housed: Our dogs will stay at *kennels* while we are on vacation.

L l

long·horn [lông′hôrn′] One of a former breed of beef cattle with long horns: A *longhorn* was a common sight in the southwestern United States.

lush [lŭsh] Full of a healthy growth of trees and plants; growing well: Their *lush* garden looked like a jungle.

lyre [līr] An instrument like a harp: While telling stories or singing, a Greek minstrel played a *lyre*.

M m

Man·ya [män′yä] A woman's name (Polish).

mas·ter [măs′tər] **mas·tered, mas·ter·ing** 1. To bring under control. 2. To become an expert in: When you have *mastered* the skills of the game, you will be a winner.

mead·ow [měd′ō] A piece of land where grass is grown for hay or for grazing: Many cattle were feeding in the green *meadow*.

mer·chan·dise [mûr′chən·dīs] Goods bought and sold to make money: A department store sells clothes, books, stoves, and other *merchandise*.

mus·cle [mŭs′əl] One of the bundles of tissue in the body that produce the body's movements: Exercise makes *muscles* strong.

N n

naph·tha [năf′thə *or* năp′thə] An oily substance used as a fuel or cleaning fluid: *Naphtha* burns easily.

nec·tar [něk′tər] In Greek myths, the drink of the gods: *Nectar* was thought to taste like honey.

nour·ish [nûr′ĭsh] **nour·ished, nour·ish·ing** To keep alive and healthy or help to grow with food: To be strong, people must eat *nourishing* food.

nov·el·ty [nŏv′əl·tē] Something different, or unusual: A number of years ago television was a *novelty*.

Nu·nuk [noŏ′nŭk′] A man's name, common in far northern North America.

O o

op·er·a [ŏp′ər·ə *or* ŏp′rə] A kind of play set to music in which all or most of the lines are sung rather than spoken: An orchestra usually plays the music for the singers in the *opera*.

or·ches·tra [ôr′kəs·trə]
A group of
musicians playing
together,
especially a large
group of
musicians playing
many different
instruments: The
musician joined
an *orchestra*.

P p

par·ka [pär′kə]
A fur or cloth coat
with a hood: In
cold places the
hooded *parka* is
worn.

phil·har·mon·ic [fĭl′här·mŏn′ĭk]
Loving music: A *philharmonic* club
may organize an orchestra.

pi·o·neer [pī′ə·nĭr′] One of the first
settlers or colonists of a new country
or region: The people who settled the
American West were *pioneers*.

pon·der [pŏn′dər] **pon·dered,
pon·der·ing** To think about or
consider carefully: They looked at a
map and began *pondering* which road
to take to the lake.

prai·rie [prâr′ē] A large area of flat,
grassy land having few or no trees:
The broad plain of central North
America is a *prairie*.

pres·sure ridge [prĕsh′ər rĭj] A
narrow hill made on ice by the force
of wind or tide: In the spring when

the ice begins to melt, the ice can
move and form a *pressure ridge*.

pri·ma don·na [prē′mə dŏn′ə] A
leading female opera or concert
singer: Only a very good singer
becomes a *prima donna*.

pub·lic re·la·tions [pŭb′lĭk
rĭ·lā′shənz] Having to do with the
business of encouraging good feeling
between customers and companies or
between people and other
institutions: The *public relations*
department explained the company's
fares.

pum·per·nick·el [pŭm′pər·nĭk′əl]
Dark bread made from unsifted rye:
Some sandwiches are made with
pumpernickel.

Q q

quick·sand [kwĭk′sănd′] A deep bed
of sand so filled and soaked with
water that it swallows up anything
that tries to move upon it: We threw a
rock into the *quicksand*, and the rock
sank quickly.

R r

rac·quet [răk′ĭt]
A light bat made
of a handle
attached to a
round frame
strung with a
network usually of
catgut or nylon: A
player hits the
ball with a
racquet.

reed [rēd] Any grass having a hollow stem: Many tall *reeds* grew at the edge of the pond.

re·venge [rĭ·vĕnj′] The act of returning punishment for a wrong received: When they broke our windows, we wanted *revenge*.

ro·tate [rō′tāt] **ro·tat·ed, ro·tat·ing** 1. To turn on an axis. 2. To take turns in order: The volleyball players *rotated* the serve.

S s

sen·ti·ment [sĕn′tə·mənt] 1. A delicate feeling. 2. A way of thinking, feeling, or seeing something: The workers had mixed *sentiments* about their jobs.

Se·quoy·ah [sĭ·kwoi′ə] 1770?–1843, a Cherokee Indian who invented the Cherokee syllabary.

se·rene [sĭ·rēn′] Peaceful; calm: After the stormy night the morning sky seemed *serene*.

shim·mer [shĭm′ər] **shim·mered, shim·mer·ing** To shine with an unsteady, glimmering light: The clean new car was *shimmering* in the heat.

si·mul·ta·ne·ous·ly [sī′məl·tā′nē·əs·lē] Happening, done, or existing at the same time: I bumped into my friend, and we dropped our books *simultaneously*.

spool [spool] A cylinder on which thread, yarn, or wire is wound: We bought a *spool* of blue thread to mend our jeans.

Stieg·litz, Al·fred [stēg′lĭts, ăl′frĕd], 1864–1946, a pioneer in photography.

stow [stō] **stowed, stow·ing** To pack in a neat, close way: The people are *stowing* their belongings in a safe place.

sub·due [sŭb·d(y)oo′] **sub·dued, sub·du·ing** 1. To get power over, as by force. 2. To hold back: We were told to be quiet, so we *subdued* our talk and laughter.

syl·la·ba·ry [sĭl′ə·bĕr′ē] A set of written symbols spelling individual syllables and not single sounds, as in an alphabet: Cherokee writing uses a *syllabary*.

sym·bol [sĭm′bəl] A mark or sign used to stand for something, as a plus sign: Letters of the alphabet are *symbols* standing for sounds.

sym·pho·ny [sĭm′fə·nē] A piece of music written to be played by a large orchestra and usually made up of four parts: A *symphony* is a long, difficult musical piece.

T t

ten·ant [tĕn′ənt] A person who rents land, a house, or an apartment from another: Some people own houses, and others are *tenants* in apartments.

the·o·ry [thē′ə·rē *or* thĭr′ē] A set of rules used in making guesses about a watched event: We saw a groundhog enter a hole in the ground and formed this *theory:* groundhogs make their homes below ground.

tour·na·ment [tŏŏr′nə·mənt *or* tûr′nə·mənt] In sports, a number of matches which come one after another and include many players: Fifteen good golfers played in the big *tournament.*

trag·e·dy [trăj′ə·dē] 1. A serious play ending unhappily. 2. A very sad happening: The car accident was a *tragedy.*

treach·er·ous [trĕch′ər·əs] Not as safe as it appears; dangerous: The path through the woods is *treacherous* at night.

tress [trĕs] A lock of hair: A long *tress* hung down her back.

U u

um·pire [ŭm′pīr] An official who rules on the plays in a sports contest, as baseball: The *umpire* called the pitch a strike.

un·em·ployed [ŭn′ĭm·ploid′] Without a job; out of work: The *unemployed* people were looking for jobs.

u·nique [yōō·nēk′] Unusual, rare: A purple car and a round house are *unique.*

V v

Val·da, Car·lo [väl′dä, kär′lō] A man's name (Spanish).

vict·uals [vĭt′(ə)lz] Food: A pioneer often had to hunt for *victuals.*

W w

wash·er [wäsh′ər *or* wôsh′ər] A flat ring of metal or rubber: The leaking faucets need new *washers.*

Wim·ble·don [wĭm′b(ə)l·dŭn] A part of London, England, where the British National Tournament is held.

wran·gler [răng′glər] A person who rounds up horses: Making sure the horses are safe and cared for is the job of a *wrangler.*

wretch·ed [rĕch′ĭd] Very unhappy or miserable: The lost dog was *wretched.*

ACKNOWLEDGMENTS

Grateful acknowledgment is given for permission to reprint the following copyrighted material:

"Baseball's Lady Manager" adapted from "Baseball's Madam Manager" by Ann DeFrange. Copyright 1978, The Oklahoma Publishing Company, *The Sunday Oklahoman*, July 30.

"Born Is Better (Or Is It?)" by Nancy Garber, adapted by permission of the author, reprinted courtesy of *Wee Wisdom* magazine.

"Circus" by Eleanor Farjeon, copyright 1926, renewed 1954 by Eleanor Farjeon. From *Poems for Children*, copyright 1951 by Eleanor Farjeon. Reprinted by permission of J. B. Lippincott Company and Harold Ober Associates Incorporated.

"Getting Even with Jimmie Ray" by Robert L. Stevenson and Rosalind E. Woodruff. Reprinted by permission of *Ebony Jr!* Magazine, copyright 1976 by Johnson Publishing Company, Inc.

"Hai Lu and the Necklace" by Bernadine Beatie. From *Jack and Jill* magazine, copyright © 1972 by The Saturday Evening Post Company, Indianapolis, Indiana. Adapted by permission of the publisher.

"Hi-Me" by Pat Clyne, adapted by permission of the author, reprinted courtesy of *Wee Wisdom* magazine.

"The Horse Who Went Fishing" by Jean Morris. From *Jack and Jill* magazine, copyright © 1973 by The Saturday Evening Post Company, Indianapolis, Indiana. Adapted by permission of the publisher.

"How the Prairie Pioneers Built Their Houses" by John I. White. Copyright © 1971, Highlights for Children, Inc., Columbus, Ohio.

"Konrad Lorenz: Mother to Birds" from "Konrad Lorenz: A Mother to Birds" by Michele Palmer. Copyright © 1974, Highlights for Children, Inc., Columbus, Ohio.

"Land of the Big Night" by Ruth A. Boellstorff. Adapted and reprinted from *Jack and Jill* magazine by permission of the author, Ruth A. Boellstorff, © 1972 The Saturday Evening Post Company, Indianapolis, Indiana.

"Learn to Play Soccer" by Tom Peterson. Adapted with permission of the author and *Boys' Life*, published by the Boy Scouts of America.

"The Mail-Order Pony" by Barbara P. Atwood. Every effort has been made to contact Barbara P. Atwood for permission to use "The Mail-Order Pony."

"Make a Racing Car" by James E. Seidelman and Grace Mintonye, adapted by permission of the authors. Formerly published in *Wee Wisdom* magazine by Grace Mintonye and James E. Seidelman. From "Seidelman Says Be a Good Sport," courtesy of *Wee Wisdom* magazine.

"More about Cowboys" adapted from the *Young Children's Encyclopedia* by permission of Encyclopaedia Britannica, Inc.

"My Mother Saw a Dancing Bear" by Charles Causley. From the book *Figgie Hobbin*, © 1973, text, by Charles Causley, published by Macmillan London, Ltd. Reprinted by permission of David Higham Associates Limited.

"Old-Time America: The Cattle Drive" by Margaret C. Moran and Joe Bolden. From *Jack and Jill* magazine, copyright © 1972 by The Saturday Evening Post Company, Indianapolis, Indiana. Adapted by permission of the publisher.

"The Other Moon" by Nancy Catalano. From *Jack and Jill* magazine, copyright © 1971 by The Jack and Jill Publishing Company, Indianapolis, Indiana. Adapted by permission of the publisher.

"The Panther" by Ogden Nash, copyright 1940 by Ogden Nash. From *The Face Is Familiar* by Ogden Nash, by permission of Little, Brown and Company. Reprinted by permission of Curtis Brown, Ltd. Copyright 1944, © 1959 by Ogden Nash.

"Quicksand" by Alan Cliburn. From *Jack and Jill* magazine, copyright © 1968 by The Curtis Publishing Company. Adapted by permission of the publisher.

"Rumpelstiltskin" from *The Straw Ox and Other Tales* by Fan Kissen. Adapted by permission of Houghton Mifflin Company, publisher.

"The Season" by Nancy Garber, adapted by permission of the author, reprinted courtesy of *Wee Wisdom* magazine.